STUDENT WORKBOOK

FOR

MULTIMEDIA STANDARD FIRST AID

1981 Edition

# ACKNOWLEDGMENTS

The content of Multimedia Standard First Aid is based on information provided by the Division of Medical Sciences, National Academy of Sciences, National Research Council (NAS, NRC). The American Heart Association cooperated in setting compatible technical standards for AHA and Red Cross materials. This edition reflects the updating of standards recommended by the 1979 National Conference on Cardiopulmonary Resuscitation and Emergency Cardiac Care.

The Red Cross thanks Sam F. Seeley, M.D., who gave technical guidance for preparation of the American Red Cross Advanced First Aid and Emergency Care textbook before his retirement as Professional Associate for the Division of Medical Sciences of NAS, NRC. Dr. Seeley's continued interest and assistance after his retirement are greatly valued by the Red Cross. The Red Cross also gives special thanks to Archer S. Gordon, M.D., Ph.D. for technical guidance and advice in developing the materials on respiratory emergencies.

The instructional research and development of the original version of Multimedia Standard First Aid (1966) were carried out by The American Institutes for Research, Palo Alto, California, Leslie J. Briggs, Ph.D., Principal Investigator, David G. Markle, Ph.D., Project Director, under contract with the Bell Telephone System. The current version of Multimedia (1981) was designed by Communication Research Laboratories, Inc., Steamboat Springs, Colorado, under the supervision of David G. Markle, Ph.D. and Nancy H. Markle, Ph.D., Co-Directors. Roseanna L. Dufault, Kathy M. Dietrich, and Patsy L. Parkin were Project Assistants; drawings are by Monica King and Scott Gorrell.

Review and guidance for technical consistency were provided by C. P. Dail, Jr., Director of First Aid Programs, American Red Cross and Don A. Sleeper, Assistant Director of First Aid Programs, American Red Cross. Film revisions were supervised by Alan Rettig, Producer, American Red Cross Production Center.

Thanks are extended to the following Red Cross chapters for assistance in testing these materials: Alexandria Chapter, Alexandria, Va; Arlington Chapter, Arlington, Va.; Berkeley Chapter, Berkeley, Calif.; Central Illinois Chapter, Peoria, Ill.; D. C. Chapter, Washington, D. C.; San Diego County Chapter, San Diego, Calif.; and Seattle-King County Chapter, Seattle, Wash. Testing was also conducted at Lothian School, Lothian, Md.

This course is dedicated to the thousands of volunteers who give their time and abilities to provide lifesaving information to the American public.

# PREFACE

Multimedia Standard First Aid is a coordinated instructional system consisting of motion picture films, instructor-led practice sessions, and this workbook. It can be given in one workday or in several shorter sessions. The Course Outline on the following pages gives the organization of the course.

When taking the course, please follow these guidelines:

- Work carefully at your own best speed in the workbook. The schedule gives most students enough time to be successful without rushing. If you do not have enough time, arrange for more time with your instructor.

- Mark your answer to each question in the book, then check your answers on the next page. If you make a mistake, mark or record the correct answer before you go ahead.

- Watch the films carefully, because you will practice almost all of what you see right after the films are shown.

## COURSE OUTLINE
## UNIT I

| | | WORKBOOK PAGES | TIME IN MINUTES |
|---|---|---|---|
| INTRODUCTION TO COURSE | | | 5 |
| WORKBOOK | Introduction to First Aid, p. 1 | 1-60 | 24 |
| | Mouth-to-Mouth Breathing, p. 9 | | |
| FILM | Mouth-to-Mouth Breathing (3:39)[1] | | 5 |
| PRACTICE 1 | Mouth-to-Mouth Breathing | | 25 |
| WORKBOOK | Obstructed Airway, p. 61 | 61-93 | 15 |
| FILM | Airway Obstruction (4:19) | | 5 |
| PRACTICE 2 | Obstructed Airway | | 15 |
| WORKBOOK | Heart Attack and Stroke, p. 95 | 95-106 | 6 |
| FILM | Direct Pressure, Elevation, and Pressure Points (5:06) | | 6 |
| PRACTICE 3 | Direct Pressure, Elevation, and Pressure Points | | 8 |
| FILM | Tourniquet (3:11) | | 4 |
| PRACTICE 4 | Tourniquet | | 8 |
| WORKBOOK | Wounds, p. 107 | 107-136 | 14 |
| | Shock, p. 121 | | |
| BREAK | 10 minutes | | 10 |

Elapsed time for Unit 1: 2 hours 30 minutes (including break)

_____

1. Exact running times for film segments are given in minutes and seconds.
   Scheduled times are longer to allow for starting and stopping film.

# COURSE OUTLINE
## UNIT 2

|  |  | WORKBOOK PAGES | TIME IN MINUTES |
|---|---|---|---|
| WORKBOOK | Poisoning, p. 137<br>Burns, p. 155 | 137-198 | 35 |
| FILM | Bandaging, Closed and Open Spiral (5:30) |  | 7 |
| PRACTICE 5 | Closed Spiral and Open Spiral Bandages |  | 12 |
| FILM | Figure Eight Bandage and Fingertip Bandage (4:39) |  | 6 |
| PRACTICE 6 | Figure Eight Bandage |  | 10 |
| FILM | Cravat Bandage, Triangle Bandage, and Arm Sling (4:13) |  | 5 |
| PRACTICE 7 | Cravat Bandage, Triangle Bandage, and Arm Sling |  | 20 |
| WORKBOOK | Head Injuries, Internal Injuries, and Gunshot Wounds, p. 199 | 199-212 | 10 |

Elapsed time for Unit 2: 1 hour 45 minutes

LUNCH BREAK

# COURSE OUTLINE
## UNIT 3

|  |  | WORKBOOK PAGES | TIME IN MINUTES |
|---|---|---|---|
| WORKBOOK | Injuries of the Eye, p. 213 | 213-236 | 13 |
|  | Infection, Tetanus, and Animal Bites, p. 221 |  |  |
| FILM | Upper Arm Splint (3:15) |  | 5 |
| PRACTICE 8 | Upper Arm Splint |  | 20 |
| FILM | Forearm Splint (2:40) |  | 4 |
| PRACTICE 9 | Forearm Splint |  | 15 |
| FILM | Ankle Splint and Kneecap Splint (4:09) |  | 5 |
| PRACTICE 10 | Ankle Splint and Kneecap Splint |  | 12 |
| WORKBOOK | Fractures, Sprains, and Strains, p. 237 | 237-274 | 21 |
|  | Fainting, Epilepsy, and Other Sources of Convulsions, p. 247 |  |  |
|  | Ill Effects of Heat and Cold, p. 253 |  |  |
| BREAK | 10 minutes |  | 10 |

Elapsed time for Unit 3:  1 hour 45 minutes (including break)

## COURSE OUTLINE
### UNIT 4

| | | WORKBOOK PAGES | TIME IN MINUTES |
|---|---|---|---|
| WORKBOOK | Escaping from Fire, p. 275 | 275-300 | 16 |
| | Electrical Emergencies, p. 283 | | |
| | Exposure to Radiation, p. 287 | | |
| | Obtaining Help in an Emergency, p. 291 | | |
| FILM | Emergency Rescue (2:25) | | 3 |
| PRACTICE 11 | Drag by Shoulders and Blanket Drag | | 8 |
| FILM | Two-Person Carry and Carry by Extremities (2:11) | | 3 |
| PRACTICE 12 | Two-Person Carry and Carry by Extremities | | 6 |
| FILM | Improvised Litter and Three-Person Hammock Carry (3:49) | | 5 |
| PRACTICE 13 | Three-Person Hammock Carry | | 8 |
| FILM | Eight-Person Lift and Litter Carry (3:16) | | 4 |
| PRACTICE 14 | Litter Carry | | 7 |
| WORKBOOK | Rescue and Transfer, p. 301 | 301-310 | 10 |
| FINAL TEST | Form A, p. 311 | 311-328 | 20 |

Elapsed time for Unit 4 and Final Test: 1 hour 30 minutes

### END OF COURSE

# UNIT  1

## INTRODUCTION TO FIRST AID

### What Is First Aid?

First aid is immediate care for victims of injuries or sudden illness.  When you give first aid, you deal with the victim's physical condition, the victim's emotional state, and the whole accident situation.  First aid also includes care needed later if medical help is delayed or is not available.

Urgent care is first aid given in life-threatening situations.  These situations include stopped breathing, heart attack and stroke, heavy bleeding, poisoning, and shock.

I

It is more important, for example, to give mouth-to-mouth breathing than it is to bandage a mild burn. In an emergency, you may have to leave someone with a broken arm alone while you save someone else from bleeding to death.

Take care of life-threatening situations first, then seek help. If several people are available, one can go for help while others help you give first aid. Do not leave people who need urgent care to get help.

Sometimes you will not need to hurry. The victim may need medical attention but not urgent care. Then your role is to prevent more injury, seek medical help, and keep the victim calm.

## Examining and Checking the Victim

Examine the victim carefully and check for injuries.  Keep checking until medical help arrives.  If you found no serious burns on your first careful examination, you should not find any later.  However, minor burns may develop blisters that need to be protected with a bandage.  A wound may start to bleed again.

Keep checking to see if the victim is conscious.  An unconscious victim may have been breathing when you checked at first but may have stopped breathing since then. Keep checking an unconscious person for breathing and heartbeat.

## Eight Topics in Emergency Action

These actions are given in the order in which you might take them in an emergency.

1. Rescue the victim and yourself.

2. Restore or maintain Breathing and Heartbeat.

3. Control heavy Bleeding.

4. Treat for Poisoning.

5. Prevent Shock.

6. Examine the victim carefully.

7. Seek Medical Help.

8. Keep Checking the victim until medical help is obtained.

1. Imagine that you are a lifeguard at a swimming pool. You rescue a small girl from the bottom of the pool. What will you check for first?

[X] a. Breathing.
[ ] b. Broken bones.
[ ] c. Poisoning.


2. Number these victims of an automobile accident in the order in which you would care for them.

_3_ A person who is trapped in a car, conscious, and seems not to be injured. The car is not burning and not in a dangerous place.

_2_ A person who is unconscious, breathing, and bleeding slightly from a wound on the arm.

_1_ A person who is not breathing.

6

Answers:

1.    a.  Check for <u>breathing</u> first.

2.    Care for the victims in this order:

  3   A person who is trapped in a car, conscious, and seems not to be injured. The car is not burning and not in a dangerous place.

  2   A person who is unconscious, breathing, and bleeding <u>slightly</u> from a wound on the arm.

  1   A person who is not breathing.

3.  The first time you check a victim, you stop heavy bleeding and bandage the wound.  Do you need to check for bleeding later?

[✓] a. Yes.
[ ] b. No.


4.  Check often to be sure that a conscious victim stays conscious. Check an unconscious victim often for

[✓] a. breathing and heartbeat.
[ ] b. consciousness.

8

Answers:

3.  a. <u>Yes</u>, check the bandage later.  The wound may start to bleed again.

4.  a. Check an unconscious victim often for <u>breathing</u> and <u>heartbeat</u>.

*    *    *

Continue in the workbook with the lesson on mouth-to-mouth breathing.

# MOUTH-TO-MOUTH BREATHING

## Is the Person Conscious?

If someone collapses, find out if he or she is conscious right away. Tap the victim's shoulder firmly or shake the victim gently and shout, "Are you OK?" A person who is conscious will respond and will <u>not</u> have stopped breathing. Check for other problems and keep checking for consciousness. Do not shake the person vigorously if there is any chance of neck or back injury.

If the victim does not respond, shout, "Help!" to get the attention of people who may be able to help you.

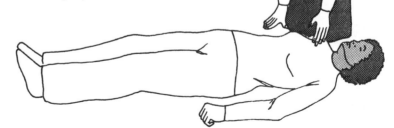

## Positioning the Victim

If the victim is unconscious, you will check for breathing. Depending on the victim's condition, you may have to give mouth-to-mouth breathing or correct a blocked airway. The victim must be lying on the back for some methods of caring for a blocked airway, and mouth-to-mouth breathing is easier to give if the victim is on the back. If the victim is lying face down or in some awkward position, you must consider injuries you can cause or make worse by moving the victim. How did the victim get here? By falling from a high ladder? By being struck by a car? As a result of passing out while having a heart attack or stroke?

If you are fairly sure that the victim collapsed without injuries, you should probably position him or her on the back right away. In caring for a victim of a violent accident, however, it is probably better to check for breathing before you move the victim at all. In many cases you can not know for sure what injuries a person has. You must use your best judgment.

Your goal is to roll the victim as a unit, all at once, without twisting any body parts. First, straighten the legs and arms so they won't get in the way. Then roll the victim toward you, onto the back.

This picture shows a method that will work in many cases—support the head and neck with one hand, and pull with the other hand just under the victim's arm. Keep the body from twisting.

Always check the breathing of an unconscious person right away. You have only a few minutes to save the life of someone whose breathing has stopped. Every moment that you wait makes recovery less likely. Permanent brain damage can occur very quickly, sometimes in less than 4 minutes.

In some emergencies, such as a fire, you may have to move the victim to a safe place before you can check for consciousness or breathing. In this section we are talking only about what to do for stopped breathing. Later we will discuss how to take care of other emergencies.

## The Airway Step

The first step for an unconscious person is the <u>Airway</u> step: tip the head back to open the airway, and check for breathing. Tip the person's head <u>way</u> <u>back</u>, until the chin points straight up. Tipping the head moves the lower jaw forward, and the tongue is attached to the lower jaw, so tipping the head moves the tongue away from the back of the throat and opens the airway. If you do not tip the head, the tongue may block the airway.

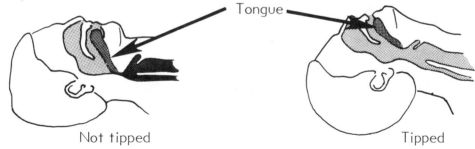

Tongue

Not tipped        Tipped

Place one hand on the victim's forehead and apply firm, backward pressure with the palm. To help tip the head way back, gently lift the victim's neck or chin with your other hand.

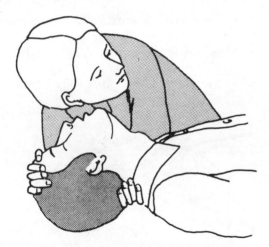

Head tip with neck lift

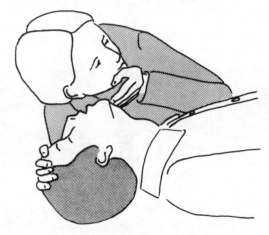

Head tip with chin lift

Head Tip with Neck Lift.  There are three important points to remember when
you tip the head with the neck lift.

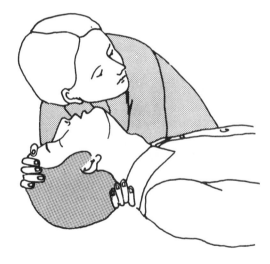

— Apply the major force with the
   hand that is on the forehead.

— Place the hand under the neck
   near the base of the skull.

— Support and lift gently with the
   hand under the neck.

As you tip the head, put your ear down near the mouth and look at the chest. <u>Look</u>, <u>listen</u>, and <u>feel</u> for breathing for about 5 seconds. If the person is breathing, you will see the chest rise and fall, hear air at the mouth and nose, and feel air on your cheek.

This picture shows checking for breathing while using the head tip—neck lift. Be sure to keep checking for about <u>5 seconds</u>.

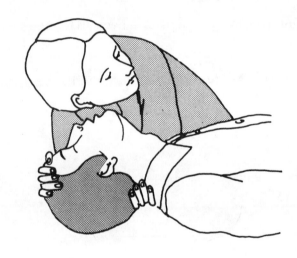

The Airway Step:

Tip Head and Check Breathing

5.  What are the two parts of the Airway step?

    ___Tip___ the head and check for ___breathing___.

6.  Which picture shows how far to tip the head?

    [ ] a.                              [✓] b.

7.  When you use the head tip—neck lift, the major force is applied
    with the hand that is

    [✓] a.  on the forehead.
    [ ] b.  under the neck.

Answers:

5.  The two parts of the Airway step are <u>tip</u> the head and check for <u>breathing</u>.

6.  b.  This picture shows how far to tip the head:

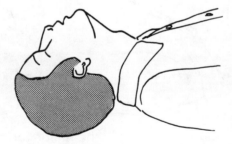

7.  a.  The major force is applied with the hand that is on the forehead.

8.  Place the hand under the neck near the

[ ]  a.  shoulders.
[✓]  b.  base of the skull.


9.  Use the hand under the neck to

[ ]  a.  lift forcefully.
[✓]  b.  support and lift gently.


10.  How do you check for breathing?

[ ]  a.  Check the pulse at the neck.
[ ]  b.  Check the pupils of the eyes.
[✓]  c.  Look at the chest; listen and feel for air coming out of the mouth.

20

Answers:

8.  b.  Place the hand under the neck near the base of the skull.

9.  b.  Use the hand under the neck to support and lift gently.

10.  c.  Look at the chest; listen and feel for air coming out of the mouth.

<u>Head Tip with Chin Lift</u>.  When you tip the head, you can use the neck lift or the chin lift.  There are five important points to remember for the chin lift.

- Apply the major force with the hand on the forehead.

- Place your fingertips under the bony part of the jaw near the chin.

- Support and lift the jaw with your fingertips, but avoid closing the mouth.

- Do not push on the soft tissues of the throat—this may block the airway.

- If necessary, pull the lower lip down slightly with your thumb to keep the mouth open.

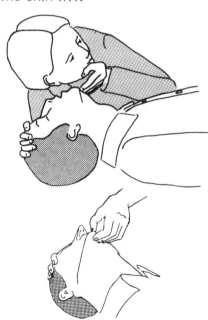

<u>How Should You Tip the Head</u>?  The head tip—neck lift is well known and has been used successfully for many years.  The head tip—chin lift has been shown to produce a better airway in some cases.  You should learn both.

When you tip the head, be sure to put your ear near the victim's mouth and look at the chest to check for breathing.  Someone who has stopped breathing may start to breathe again when you tip the head.

23

11.    What is the Airway step?  Tip the head and check for breathing for about

[ ]    a.  one second.
[x]    b.  5 seconds.


12.    When you do the head tip—chin lift, place your fingertips under the

[x]    a.  bony part of the jaw near the chin.
[ ]    b.  soft part of the throat near the chin.


13.    Which picture shows how to do the chin lift?

[ ] a.                      [x] b. 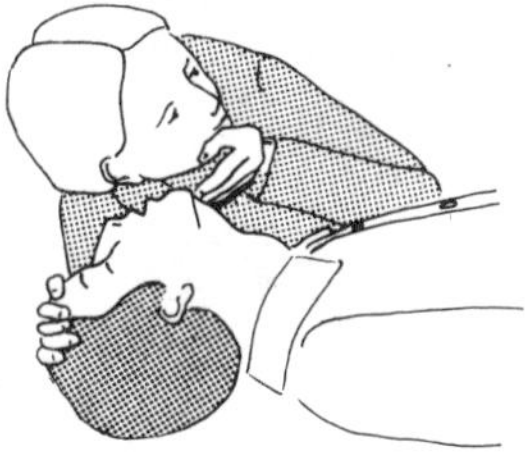                      [ ] c.

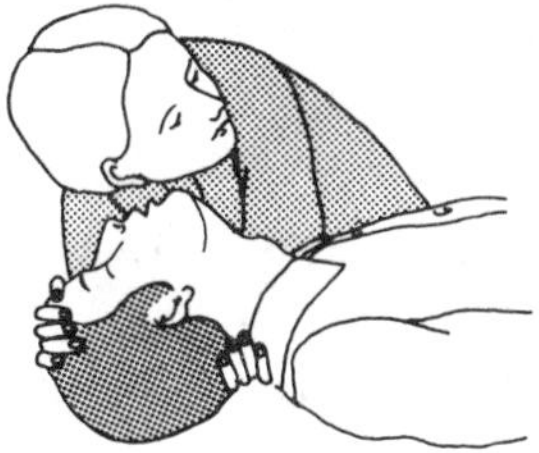

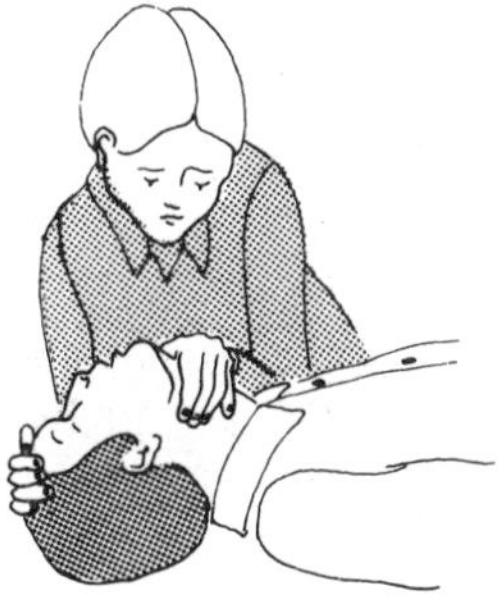

Answers:

11.  b.  The Airway step is to tip the head and check for breathing for about 5 seconds.

12.  a.  When you do the head tip—chin lift, place your fingertips under the bony part of the jaw near the chin.

13.  b.  This picture shows how to do the chin lift.

## The Quick Step

If the person is not breathing, give 4 quick, full breaths.  This is called the Quick step.

Keep the head tipped.  Pinch the nose so air will not come out the nose when you blow into the mouth.  Take a deep breath and open your mouth wide.  Cover the victim's mouth with your mouth.  Make a good seal.

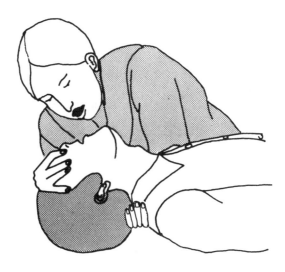

Give 4 <u>big</u> breaths as fast as you can, without letting the lungs deflate between breaths. Remove your mouth from the victim's mouth between breaths just long enough to get a fast gulp of air for the next breath.

Give breaths right on top of each other, without pauses. This expands the lungs fully and gives a lot of oxygen quickly.

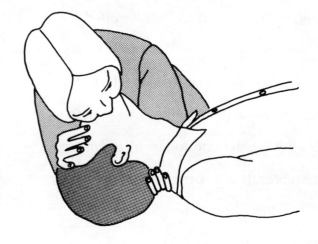

The Quick Step:

4 Quick Breaths

14.   Fill in the two parts of the Airway step:

Airway: _____ and _____

15.   The 4 quick breaths should be

[ ]   a.   small breaths.
[✗]   b.   full breaths.

16.   How long do you pause between each of the 4 quick breaths?

[ ]   a.   About 3 seconds between each breath.
[✗]   b.   Only long enough to get a breath.

Answers:

14.   Airway:  <u>tip the head</u> and <u>check for breathing</u>.

15.   b.  Give <u>full</u> breaths.

16.   b.  Pause <u>only long enough to get a breath</u> between each of the 4 quick breaths.

## The Check Step

After you give 4 quick breaths, check the pulse and check for breathing again. This is called the <u>Check</u> step. To help remember the first steps for an unconscious person, use the phrase "A Quick Check".

<u>A</u> = <u>A</u>irway:  Tip the head and check for breathing.

<u>Quick</u> = Give 4 <u>quick</u>, full breaths.

<u>Check</u> = <u>Check</u> the pulse and breathing.

Check the pulse on the side of the neck near you. Keep the head tipped with your hand on the forehead. Place the fingertips of your other hand on the Adam's apple, then slide your fingers into the groove at the side of the neck. Check the pulse and breathing for at least 5 seconds but no more than 10 seconds.

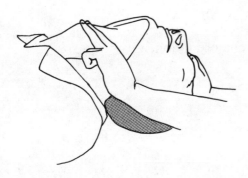

Start here.

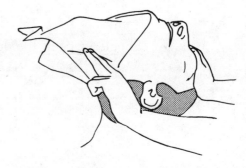

Check pulse here.

Find your own neck pulse now.

17. Where do you find the pulse?

[X] a. In the groove at the side of the neck.
[ ] b. On top of the Adam's apple.

18. Check the pulse and breathing for at least ___~~to~~ 5___ seconds.

19. What are the steps for A Quick Check?

A = Airway: __Tip the head__ and check __for breathing__.

Quick = Give ___4 full breaths___.

Check = Check the __pulse__ and check __for breathing__.

Answers:

17.  a.  Find the pulse in the groove at the <u>side</u> of the neck.

18.  Check the pulse and breathing for at least <u>5</u> seconds.

19.  The steps for A Quick Check are:

A = Airway:  <u>Tip the head</u> and <u>check for breathing</u>.

Quick = Give <u>4 quick breaths</u>.

Check = Check the <u>pulse</u> and <u>breathing</u>.

Please read about the EMS system on the inside front cover of this book now, if you have not done so already. Then continue on this page.

If the person is not breathing but <u>has</u> a pulse, give mouth-to-mouth breathing. If the person is not breathing and <u>does not have</u> a pulse, cardiopulmonary resuscitation (CPR) is needed and the EMS system should be activated. If you have not been trained in CPR, give mouth-to-mouth breathing. The heart may be beating even though you did not find a pulse, so mouth-to-mouth breathing may keep the person alive. If you are not scheduled to study CPR, sign up to do so soon.

Get ready to give more breaths this way:

1) Be sure the head is still tipped.
2) Pinch the nose shut again.
3) Take a deep breath, open your mouth wide, and make a tight seal over the victim's mouth.

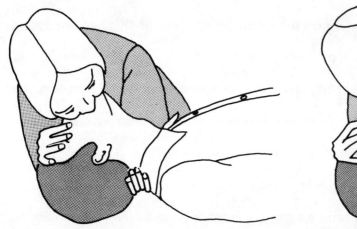

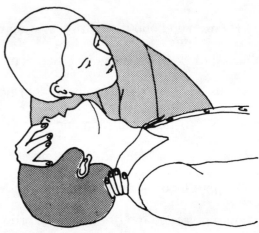

Blow to fill up the lungs.
Watch the chest rise.

Listen and feel for air.
Watch the chest fall.

Do these steps once every 5 seconds.  It may help to count, "One, one-thousand;

two, one-thousand; three, one-thousand; four, one-thousand; b-r-e-a-t-h-e."

20. How do you count for one breath every 5 seconds?

[ ] a. "One-and, two-and, three-and, four-and, b-r-e-a-t-h-e."
[X] b. "One, one-thousand; two, one-thousand; three, one-thousand; four, one-thousand; b-r-e-a-t-h-e."

21. When you take a breath, turn your head to look at the victim's

[X] a. chest.
[ ] b. forehead.

22. What phrase will help you to remember the first steps for an unconscious person?

One    quick    check

Answers:

20.  b.  Count, "One, one-thousand; two, one-thousand; three, one-thousand; four, one-thousand; b-r-e-a-t-h-e," for one breath every 5 seconds.

21.  a.  Turn your head to look at the victim's <u>chest</u> while you take another breath.

22.  Give an unconscious person <u>A Quick Check</u>.

After a victim starts to breathe again, watch to be sure he or she keeps breathing.

Give care to prevent shock:

— Keep the victim lying down and at a comfortable temperature.

— Raise the feet and legs if moving the legs does not cause injury or pain.

— Raise the head <u>and</u> shoulders if the victim has trouble breathing or has a head injury. Do not put the head on a pillow, because this may bend the neck and block the airway. Do not raise the head or shoulders if you suspect a neck or back injury.

Call a doctor or ambulance, or take the victim to a hospital or life-support unit.

In some cases, a person can be kept alive with mouth-to-mouth breathing but will not start breathing without medical treatment. Mouth-to-mouth breathing may be needed for a very long time. Keep giving mouth-to-mouth breathing until the victim recovers, medical personnel take over, or you are certain the victim is dead.

## Mouth-to-Nose Breathing

Sometimes you cannot make a good seal over the mouth:

- Air may leak out when you blow.

- The victim's mouth or jaw may be injured.

- The victim's jaws may be shut tight so that
  you cannot open the mouth to give a breath.

- Your mouth may be too small.

If you cannot make a good mouth-to-mouth seal, give mouth-to-nose breathing.

Hand positions for mouth-to-nose breathing:

Step 1:  Tip the head.  Use either the neck lift or the chin lift.

Step 2:  Close the mouth.

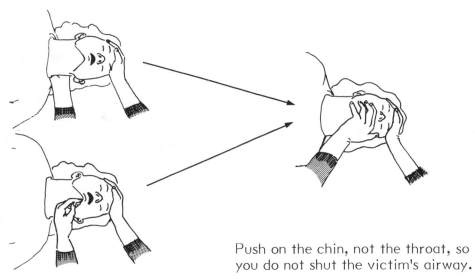

Push on the chin, not the throat, so you do not shut the victim's airway.

Blow into the nose.

Then open the mouth and listen for air. Watch the chest fall.

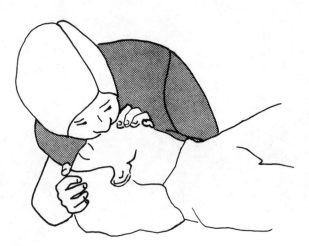

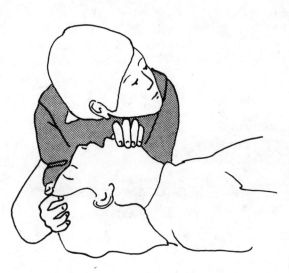

23. While you blow into the <u>nose</u>, what do you do with the person's mouth?

[X] a. Close the mouth.
[ ] b. Open the mouth.

24. Fill in the first steps for mouth-to-mouth (or mouth-to-nose) breathing:

A = Airway: _Tip the head_ and _check for breathing_

Quick = _4 full breaths_ .

Check = _pulse_ and _breathing_ .

Answers:

23.   a.   <u>Close</u> the person's mouth while you blow into the nose.

24.   A = Airway:   <u>Tip the head and check breathing.</u>

Quick = <u>Give 4 quick breaths.</u>

Check = <u>Check the pulse and breathing.</u>

## Air in the Stomach

When you are giving mouth-to-mouth breathing, the victim's stomach may fill up with air. Air in the stomach can push against the lungs, making it difficult or impossible to give full breaths. You can expel the air by pushing on the stomach, but this is dangerous to do because the victim may vomit and inhale the vomit into the lungs. When you give breaths, try to blow just hard enough to make the chest rise, because you are likely to force air into the stomach if you blow too hard.

If the stomach is bulging with air and you can not inflate the lungs, take these steps:

1) Turn the victim on one side.
2) Push on the stomach with your hand between the rib cage and the waist.
3) Clean out the mouth if the victim vomits.
4) Roll the victim onto the back and continue mouth-to-mouth breathing.

Take these steps only if air in the stomach is keeping you from giving breaths.

## Dentures

It may be hard to make a good mouth-to-mouth seal on a person who wears dentures (false teeth) if the dentures slip out of place and allow the lips to cave in. Try to hold dentures in place by holding the chin up with the chin lift.

If you can not hold the dentures in place, take them out and give mouth-to-mouth breathing or mouth-to-nose breathing.

## Mouth-to-Stoma Breathing

About 25,000 persons in the United States have had part or all of the larynx (voice box) removed by surgery. These people breathe through an opening in the front of the neck (a stoma), so mouth-to-stoma breathing is used for them.

A person with a temporary stoma may have a passage from the lungs to the mouth and nose, so you may need to block the mouth and nose when you blow in the stoma. If the lungs do not inflate when you blow in the stoma, block the mouth and nose with your hand.

A person may wear a breathing tube in a stoma. If the tube is clogged, it is safe to remove it with the fingers to open the airway. Send the tube with the victim to the hospital, or allow the victim to clean and replace it. The rescuer should not replace the tube.

46

When giving mouth-to-stoma breathing,

- do not tip the head.  Keep the head and neck straight.

- check breathing with your ear near the stoma.

- give breaths with your mouth sealed over the stoma.

- block the mouth and nose if air escapes from them when
  you blow in the stoma.

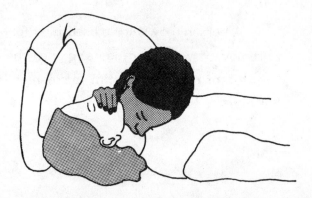

25.   How do you place the head for mouth-to-stoma breathing?

[ ]   a.   Tipped back.
[X]   b.   Straight.


26.   Where is a stoma located?

[X]   a.   The front of the neck.
[ ]   b.   The side of the neck.
[ ]   c.   The back of the neck.

Answers:

25.  b.  Keep the head <u>straight</u> for mouth-to-stoma breathing.

26.  a.  A stoma is at the <u>front</u> of the neck.

## Babies and Children

Mouth-to-mouth breathing, CPR, and first aid for airway obstructions are similar for adults and children, but some changes are needed for the smaller sizes and faster breathing and heartbeats of children. In discussing methods for young people, we will call anyone under one year of age a "baby" and anyone between one year and eight years a "child". Methods for adults should be used on those older than eight. These guidelines are approximate. In an emergency, use your best judgment—do not try to be exact about age because a slight difference will not be critical.

Checking Consciousness. Check consciousness the same way as for an adult: tap or gently shake a baby or child, and shout. If the victim is unconscious, do A Quick Check.

The Airway Step. Put one hand on the forehead and the other hand (or as many fingers as will easily fit) under the neck. Tip a baby's head gently, not as far as an adult's. Put your ear down close to the mouth and look at the chest. Look, listen, and feel for breathing.

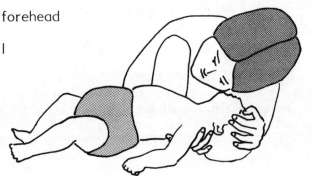

The Quick Step. If there is no breathing, give the Quick step. Keep the head tipped. Open your mouth wide and put it over the mouth and nose of a baby or child. If a child is too large for you to make a good seal over the mouth and nose, pinch the nose and make a seal over the mouth, as for an adult.

Give a baby four <u>quick</u>, <u>gentle</u> <u>puffs</u>. A puff is about the amount of air you can hold in your cheeks. Remove your mouth from the baby to get each new puff, but do not pause between the 4 quick puffs.

Give a child 4 quick, gentle breaths. Give enough air to make the chest rise.

If the head tip—neck lift does not open the airway, use the head tip—chin lift method.

The Check Step.  After the Quick step, do the Check step.  Check the pulse of a baby with your fingertips on the inside of the upper arm.  Place the tips of two fingers halfway between the elbow and the shoulder.  Place your thumb on the opposite side of the arm, and squeeze gently.  Check the pulse of a child at the neck, just as for an adult. Check for at least 5 seconds, but not more than 10 seconds.

Keep your ear near the victim's mouth and look at the chest to check breathing again while you check the pulse.

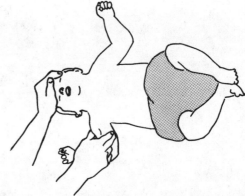

27. How far do you tip a baby's head?

[X] a. Not as far as an adult's.
[ ] b. As far as an adult's.


28. Put your mouth over a baby's

[ ] a. mouth or nose.
[X] b. mouth and nose.


29. Give a baby

[X] a. 4 quick, full breaths.
[X] b. 4 quick, gentle puffs.


30. Check a baby's pulse with your fingertips

[X] a. on the inside of the upper arm.
[ ] b. on the outside of the upper arm.

Answers:

27.  a.  Tip a baby's head gently, <u>not as far</u> as an adult's.

28.  b.  Put your mouth over a baby's <u>mouth and nose</u>.

29.  b.  Give a baby 4 quick <u>gentle</u> <u>puffs</u>.

30.  a.  Check a baby's pulse on the inside of the upper arm.

If a baby is <u>not</u> breathing but <u>does</u> have a pulse, give mouth-to-mouth-and-nose breathing. Give one puff every 3 seconds—faster than for an adult. You can count, "One, one-thousand; two, one-thousand; b-r-e-a-t-h-e."

Give a child one breath every 4 seconds—slower than for a baby but faster than for an adult. When you open the airway, the victim may struggle to breathe or breathe weakly. If the victim does not seem to be getting enough oxygen, give breaths. Time your breaths with the victim's efforts to breathe. One sign of not enough oxygen is blue lips.

If the victim is not breathing and does not have a pulse, CPR is needed and the EMS system should be activated. If you have not been trained in CPR, give mouth-to-mouth breathing. The heart may be beating even though you did not feel it.

When you give breaths, the stomach may fill up with air.  This happens more often with babies and children than with adults.  It is caused by blowing too hard or by a partially blocked airway.  If the stomach seems to be filling with air, check that the head is tipped and that you are not blowing too hard.  If air in the stomach keeps you from giving breaths, take these steps:

1)  Turn the victim on one side.
2)  Push on the stomach with your hand between the rib cage and the waist.
3)  Clean out the mouth if the victim vomits.
4)  Roll the victim onto the back and continue mouth-to-mouth breathing.

Take these steps only if the stomach is bulging with air and you cannot inflate the lungs.  It is dangerous to push on the stomach because the victim may vomit and inhale the vomit into the lungs.

When you give breaths, try to blow just hard enough to make the chest rise, because you are likely to force air into the stomach if you blow too hard.

31.   After giving A Quick Check, give one puff to a baby every

[X]   a.   3 seconds.
[ ]   b.   5 seconds.


32.   How big is a puff?

[ ]   a.   A fairly large breath.
[X]   b.   The amount of air you can hold in your cheeks.


33.   Describe the first steps of mouth-to-mouth breathing:

A = Airway: _Tip the head_ and _check for breathing._

Quick = _Y full breaths_.

Check = _pulse_ and _breathing_.

Answers:

31.   a.  Give a baby one puff every <u>3</u> seconds.


32.   b.  A puff is the amount of air you can hold in your cheeks.


33.   A = Airway:  Tip the head and check for breathing.
      Quick = Give 4 quick breaths (puffs for babies).
      Check = Check the pulse and breathing.

\*          \*          \*

Now you will see the film about mouth-to-mouth breathing.

\*          \*          \*

   This workbook was revised in 1981 to reflect the recommendations of the 1979 National Conference on Cardiopulmonary Resuscitation and Emergency Cardiac Care. The film that you are about to see was not revised when this workbook was printed, so it does not include all of the steps that you have just read about.  However, the steps that it does show are correct.  Also, the names of some procedures, such as the finger sweep, are different.  If you see any differences between the film and the workbook, follow the directions in the workbook.

# OBSTRUCTED AIRWAY

## Conscious Victim

You may see someone choke on food, or you may suspect choking if a person collapses while eating.  Signs of breathing difficulty are wheezing, gasping, choking, coughing, and grasping the throat.

If the person is not coughing, ask, "Can you speak?"  A person who has a completely blocked airway <u>cannot breathe, cough, or speak.</u>

If the airway is almost completely blocked, there are high-pitched noises when inhaling, great difficulty breathing, and very weak or no coughing.  First aid is the same for a completely blocked airway and for one that is almost completely blocked.

Someone who is coughing forcefully should be let entirely alone.  Watch closely and encourage the person to cough.  Normal coughing is more effective than any method taught in this lesson, so do not interfere.  Do not give back blows or anything else.

If the person <u>can speak</u>, do not try to remove an object from the airway.

34.  A person who coughs forcefully should be

[ ]  a. given care for a completely blocked airway.
[X]  b. let alone and watched.


35.  A person who coughs weakly and has great difficulty breathing should be

[X]  a. given care for a completely blocked airway.
[ ]  b. let alone and watched.


36.  If a person is in distress, is not coughing, but can speak,

[ ]  a. try to remove an object from the airway.
[X]  b. do not try to remove an object from the airway.

64

Answers:

34.  b.  A person who coughs forcefully <u>should be let alone and watched</u>.

35.  a.  A person who coughs weakly and has great difficulty breathing should be given care for a <u>completely blocked airway</u>.

36.  b.  Do <u>not</u> try to remove an object from the airway if the person <u>can</u> speak.

If the victim's airway is blocked, give 4 back blows right away, then 4 thrusts.

Back blows. Stand just behind and to the side of a victim who is standing or sitting. Support the victim with one hand on the chest. The victim's head should be lower than the chest if possible, so gravity will help remove the object. Give 4 sharp blows over the spine, between the shoulder blades, as rapidly as possible. Hit with the heel of your hand, hard enough to knock the object loose.

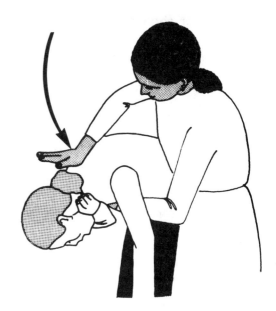

If 4 back blows do not dislodge the object, give 4 thrusts. Give thrusts either to the upper abdomen (abdominal thrusts) or to the lower chest (chest thrusts).

Abdominal Thrusts. Give abdominal thrusts in the midline of the abdomen, between the waist and the bottom edge of the rib cage. Never push on the edge of the rib cage or on the xiphoid, because you may injure the victim.

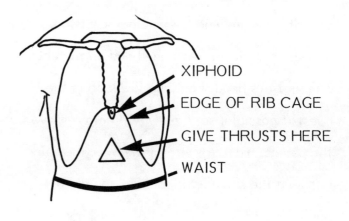

XIPHOID

EDGE OF RIB CAGE

GIVE THRUSTS HERE

WAIST

To give 4 abdominal thrusts, put

this side of your fist . . .

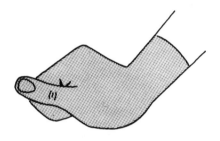

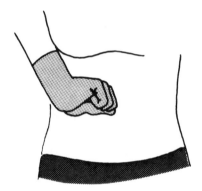

against the midline of the abdomen,

between the rib cage and the waist.

Grasp your fist with your other hand and press it into the victim's abdomen with a quick inward and upward thrust. Repeat 4 times if required.

If back blows and thrusts do not work at first, repeat the series of 4 back blows and 4 thrusts as long as the victim is conscious. Don't give up!

If the victim starts to cough forcefully, stop giving back blows and thrusts. Encourage the victim to cough.

37. When you give abdominal thrusts, what part of your fist do you place against the victim?

[ ] a. The palm side.
[x] b. The thumb side.

38. Where do you place your fist?

[ ] a. Over the edge of the rib cage.
[x] b. Between the rib cage and the waist.

39. Abdominal thrusts are given quickly,

[x] a. inward and upward.
[ ] b. straight back.

70

Answers:

37.   b.   Place the <u>thumb</u> side of your fist against the victim.

38.   b.   Place your fist <u>between the rib cage and the waist</u>.

39.   a.   Abdominal thrusts are given quickly, <u>inward</u> and <u>upward</u>.

If your airway becomes completely blocked, you will not be able to speak. Let people who are nearby know right away, before you pass out. Hold one hand to your throat— this is the "distress signal of choking."

If you are alone, give yourself thrusts. Press your fist between your rib cage and waist with a quick, inward and upward thrust, or lean forward and press your abdomen quickly over any firm object, such as the back of a chair or a porch railing.

Chest Thrusts. Reach around the chest from behind, with your arms directly under the victim's armpits. Place the thumb side of your fist on the middle of the sternum at about the level of the armpits. Grasp your fist with your other hand, and pull straight back with quick thrusts.

If the victim is in advanced pregnancy or so large that you cannot reach around the waist, give chest thrusts, not abdominal thrusts. If the victim is older and likely to have brittle bones, it is better to give abdominal thrusts to avoid injury to the ribs.

## Unconscious Victim

The first step for an unconscious person is the Airway step—tip the head and check for breathing.  If the person is not breathing normally, try to give breaths.  If air will go into the lungs, give 4 quick breaths.  Then check the pulse and breathing.

If air will not go into the lungs when you try to give the 4 quick breaths, retip the head and try again—you may not have tipped the head far enough, and the tongue may be blocking the airway.  If you still cannot get air into the lungs, an object is probably blocking the airway.  Take these steps:

1) 4 back blows.
2) 4 thrusts.
3) Sweep your finger through the mouth (finger sweep).
4) Try again to give breaths.

Try to remember, "Breaths, blows, thrusts, sweep."

**Back Blows.** Roll the victim toward you against your knees, by pulling at the hip and shoulder. Hit the victim with the heel of your hand, 4 times, over the spine, between the shoulder blades. Give the blows as rapidly as possible. Hit hard enough to knock the object loose.

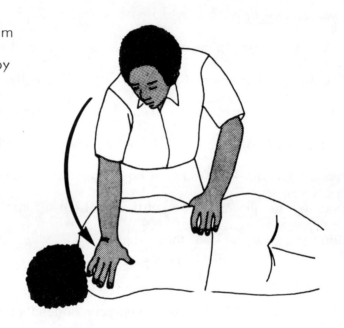

40.  If you cannot inflate the lungs the first time you try to give breaths,

[X]  a.  retip the head and try again.
[ ]  b.  give 4 back blows.


41.  Which way do you roll an unconscious victim to give back blows?

[X]  a.  Toward you.
[ ]  b.  Away from you.

Answers:

40.   a.  <u>Retip the head</u> and try again if you cannot inflate the lungs the
          first time you try to give breaths.

41.   a.  Roll the person <u>toward you</u> for back blows.

Right after you give 4 back blows, roll the victim onto the back and give 4 abdominal thrusts or 4 chest thrusts.

Abdominal Thrusts.  Put the heel of one hand on the victim's abdomen, between the rib cage and waist.  Then put your other hand on top of the first.  Point the fingers of the bottom hand toward the head.  With your shoulders directly over the victim's abdomen, press inward and upward with 4 quick thrusts.  Do not press to either side because you may injure the victim.  You may kneel astride the victim's hips or one thigh, as shown here, or alongside the victim, as shown on the next page.

Abdominal thrusts can be given from alongside the victim as well as from astride the victim.  Each position has advantages:

- Astride:  may be easier to push straight; may be easier for small rescuer.

- Alongside:  rescuer does not have to move from astride the victim to give back blows, sweep the mouth, and give breaths.

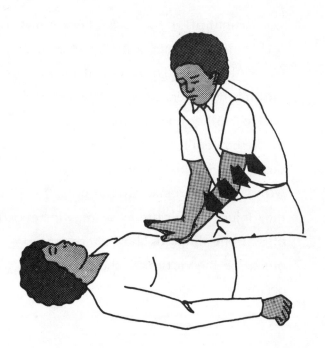

<u>Chest Thrusts</u>. The chest thrust is an alternative to the abdominal thrust for unconscious victims as well as for conscious victims.

For giving chest thrusts to an unconscious person, the body position and hand position are the same as for chest compressions in CPR. See the next two pages for a description of how to find the correct hand position.

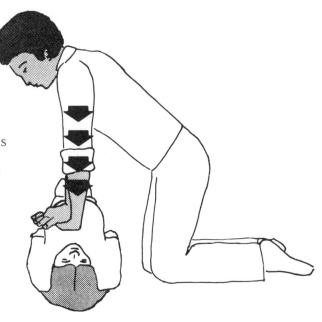

<u>Finding Where to Give Chest Thrusts</u>.  Find the lower edge of the victim's rib cage on the side near you.  Use your hand that is nearer the victim's feet.

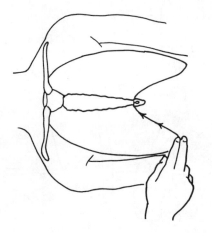 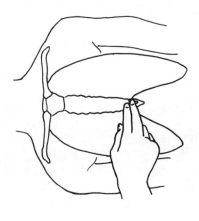

With the middle and index fingers, trace the edge of the ribs up to the notch where the ribs meet the sternum.  Keep your middle finger on the notch and place your index finger next to it on the lower end of the sternum.

Put the heel of your other hand on the sternum next to your fingers. Put the hand you measured with on top. Push straight down. Keep your fingers off the chest.

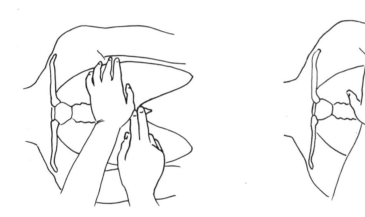

If you push on the xiphoid by mistake, it may bend in and injure the liver. It is better to be too high on the sternum than too low.

<u>Finger Sweep</u>.  After giving 4 thrusts, grasp the tongue and lower jaw between your thumb and fingers, and pull up.

With the index finger of your other hand, follow down along the inside of one cheek, deep into the throat to the base of the tongue.  Sweep in from the side.  Do not poke straight in, because that may push the object down. Use a hooking action, across toward the other cheek, to loosen and remove the object.

For an unconscious victim, remember, "Breaths, blows, thrusts, sweep."

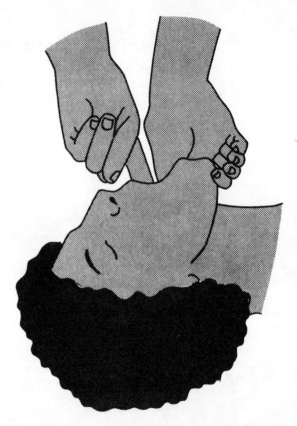

42. To give abdominal thrusts, place the heel of one hand

[ ] a. over the edge of the rib cage.
[X] b. between the rib cage and the waist.


43. Place your other hand on top of the first hand and give the thrusts

[ ] a. straight toward the ground.
[X] b. upward, toward the lungs.


44. You give 4 back blows and 4 thrusts to an unconscious victim. After giving the thrusts, you

[X] a. sweep in the mouth.
[ ] b. give 4 more back blows.

84

Answers:

42.   b.  Place the heel of one hand <u>between the rib cage and the waist</u>.

43.   b.  Thrust <u>upward</u>, toward the lungs.

44.   a.  <u>Sweep</u> after giving thrusts.

45. Try to remove the object by

[X] a. sweeping from the side.
[ ] b. poking straight into the throat.

46. If you <u>can</u> force air into the lungs but think there may be an object in the airway,

[ ] a. stop giving breaths and try to remove the object.
[X] b. keep giving breaths.

47. You have retipped a victim's head but still cannot blow air into the lungs. Number the steps to show the order in which you will do them.

_3_ Finger sweep.

_2_ 4 thrusts.

_1_ 4 back blows.

Answers:

45.   a.  Sweep your index finger in from the side.

46.   b.  <u>Keep giving breaths</u> if you can inflate the lungs.

47.   Do the steps in this order:

  _3_   Finger sweep.
  _2_   4 thrusts.
  _1_   4 back blows.

After sweeping in the mouth, whether or not you remove the object, tip the head and try to give breaths. If air will not go into the lungs, repeat 4 back blows, 4 thrusts, and sweeping. Then try again to give breaths. Keep repeating this sequence: breaths, blows, thrusts, sweep. After the victim has been without oxygen awhile, muscles in the throat relax. Methods that did not work at first may work later.

Sweep after giving thrusts. Also sweep whenever you see an object in the mouth or throat of an unconscious victim.

A victim who is given mouth-to-mouth breathing, back blows, or thrusts may vomit. Roll a victim who vomits toward you on one side and clean out the mouth with your fingers. Then roll the victim back and continue.

88

## Removing a Foreign Object, Baby or Child.

The basic steps for removing an object from the airway of a baby or child are the same as for an adult; if conscious—blows and thrusts; if unconscious—breaths, blows, thrusts, sweep.

Back Blows.  Lay a baby face down, straddling your arm, with the head lower than the chest.  Support the head with your hand around the jaw and under the chest.  Rest your arm on your thigh.  Give blows rapidly between the shoulder blades with the heel of your hand.

Place a larger child face down over your knees or something else, with the head lower than the chest.

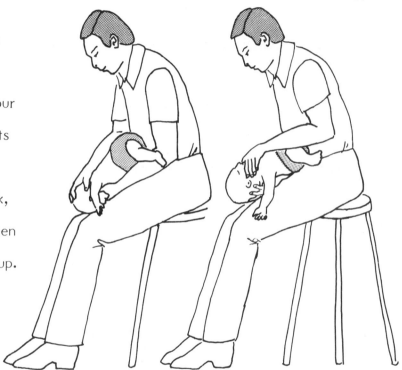

Turning a Baby Over.  Place your free hand on the baby's back and sandwich the baby between your hands and arms.  One hand supports the chest, neck, and jaw, and the other hand supports the back, neck, and head.  Holding the baby between your hands and arms, turn it face up.  Rest your arm on your thigh so the head is lower than the chest.

Chest Thrusts. Push on the chest
4 times with your fingertips on the sternum
between the nipples.  Your hand should come
in from the side, as shown here, so that your
fingertips run up and down the sternum,
not across it.

Give chest thrusts to a child
the same way you give chest thrusts
to an adult, but use only one hand and
do not push as hard.  Your arm should
come in from the side and the heel of
your hand should run up and down the
sternum.  Press straight down.

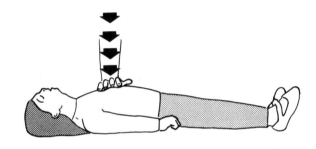

If the baby or child is conscious, keep repeating 4 back blows and 4 thrusts until
the object is expelled or the baby or child becomes unconscious.  When you turn a baby
over again for back blows, sandwich it between your hands and arms just as you did the
first time you turned it over.

92

If the victim is unconscious, think, "Breaths, blows, thrusts, sweep." First try to give breaths, then 4 back blows, then 4 chest thrusts, then sometimes a finger sweep.

Finger Sweep. Because a baby or child has a small mouth, it is easy to push an object down further by sweeping. First, place your thumb in the mouth on the tongue and place your fingers around the chin. Lift the jaw and look in the mouth. If you see an object, remove it with a finger. Do not sweep unless you see an object.

Give Breaths. Whether or not you remove an object by sweeping, start over with "give breaths." If the victim is breathing when you tip the head to give breaths, stop! If the victim is not breathing and you can give breaths, just keep giving breaths. If you cannot inflate the lungs, then give 4 back blows, 4 thrusts, finger sweep (if you can see the object) and try again to give breaths. Keep trying!

Important: If you can inflate the lungs of any victim—baby, child, or adult—give breaths even if the person had a blocked airway a few moments earlier. If you can give breaths, do not look for or try to remove a foreign object.

\* \* \*

Now you will see the film about airway obstruction.

If you see any differences between the

film and the workbook, follow the

directions in the workbook.

# HEART ATTACK AND STROKE

## Signals of Heart Attack

A person of any age may have a heart attack.  The most frequent victims of heart attack (cardiac arrest) are persons who are overweight, those who smoke, and older persons.

The most common signal that someone is having a heart attack is uncomfortable pressure, squeezing, fullness, or pain in the center of the chest.  Sometimes the pain is in the upper abdomen and seems to be indigestion.  Pain may travel out from the center of the chest to the shoulders and arms, neck and jaw.  Other signals are sweating, nausea, shortness of breath, and a feeling of weakness.

Anyone who has persistent signals of heart attack should get medical care at once. Call the paramedics or rescue squad or take the person to a hospital right away. If you think you may be going to have a heart attack, get help immediately. Have someone take you to a hospital if possible.

## Cardiopulmonary Resuscitation (CPR)

The heart and lungs work together.  The air that is breathed into the lungs gives oxygen to the blood.  The heart circulates blood, carrying oxygen to the brain and to the rest of the body.  There are many conditions that can cause the heart to stop beating (cardiac arrest).  These include all accidents that cause breathing to stop, as well as heart attacks.

If a person stops breathing, the heart may keep beating for a while.  In this case, mouth-to-mouth breathing is needed.  If a heart attack, illness, or injury makes the heart stop beating, breathing will not continue.  In this case, CPR is needed.

In <u>cardiopulmonary</u> <u>resuscitation</u>, <u>cardio</u> refers to the heart and <u>pulmonary</u> refers to the lungs.  CPR is the combination of mouth-to-mouth breathing, which supplies oxygen to the lungs, and chest compressions, which circulate blood.  By giving CPR, you breathe and circulate blood for a person whose heart and lungs have stopped working.  The purpose of CPR is to keep a person alive until the heart and lungs start working again, or until medical help is obtained.

If you have not taken a course in CPR, we urge you to do so.  CPR should be given only by persons who are properly trained.

48. Name three signals that a person is having a heart attack
and should get help right away.

1. _nausea_

2. _pain in chest_

3. _shortness of breath_

49. Can cardiac arrest be caused by an accident?

[X] a. Yes.
[ ] b. No.

50. Can people of any age have cardiac arrest?

[X] a. Yes.
[ ] b. No.

Answers:

48. Signals of a heart attack:

    1. Pressure, squeezing, fullness, or pain in the center of the chest.
    2. Pain traveling out to the shoulders, arms, neck, and jaw.
    3. Weakness, nausea, and sweating.

49. a. Yes. Cardiac arrest can be caused by an accident.

50. a. Yes. People of any age can have cardiac arrest.

## Stroke

A stroke is usually caused by a blood clot or by bleeding in the brain. Serious brain damage may produce unconsciousness, heavy breathing, and paralysis on one side of the body. The pupils of the eyes may be of unequal size.

If a stroke is slight, there may be dizziness or headache, sudden failure of memory, change of mood, muscular difficulty, difficulty speaking, or ringing in the ears.

First aid for a stroke is to keep the victim lying down, maintain normal body temperature, and get medical help immediately. Do not give anything to eat or drink.

Place a person who is unconscious or partly conscious on one side to allow fluids to drool from the mouth. If necessary, give mouth-to-mouth breathing (or CPR, if it is needed and you are trained).

When any signs of a stroke appear suddenly, especially in older persons, you should:

— protect the victim against accidents and physical exertion.

— suggest medical attention.

51. A man says that he is having trouble handling his tools. His speech is garbled and doesn't make sense. You know he has <u>not</u> been drinking.

[ ] a. Suspect that he is not telling the truth.
[x] b. Suspect a mild stroke.


52. Check all of the things to do for a person who has a severe stroke:

[x] a. Position lying down on the back or on the side.
[ ] b. Give plenty of fluids to drink.
[x] c. Maintain normal body temperature.
[ ] d. Bandage the head.
[x] e. Get medical help immediately.
[x] f. Give mouth-to-mouth breathing if necessary.

Answers:

51.   b.  Suspect a mild stroke.


52.   First aid for a severe stroke:

[X]   a.  Position lying down on the back or on the side.
[ ]   b.  Give plenty of fluids to drink.
[X]   c.  Maintain normal body temperature.
[ ]   d.  Bandage the head.
[X]   e.  Get medical help immediately.
[X]   f.  Give mouth-to-mouth breathing if necessary.

Some ways to help prevent heart attack and stroke are:

— Have a medical checkup every year after the age of 40.

— Do not smoke.

— Control your weight.

— Do not exercise strenuously if you are not used to it.

— Get adequate rest.

This is the end of instruction in topics related to breathing and blood circulation in this course.  We urge you to take a Red Cross course in CPR if you have not already done so.

\*     \*     \*

Now you will see the film about first aid for wounds.

# WOUNDS

The objectives of first aid for serious wounds are to stop the bleeding, protect wounds from contamination and infection, give care to prevent shock, and get medical help.

## Direct Pressure and Elevation

Direct pressure and elevation will stop bleeding from most wounds. <u>Always use direct pressure</u>. Use a thick pad of cloth. Press hard. If you cannot get a pad right away, apply direct pressure with your bare hand until you get a pad. Elevate the wound when you apply direct pressure if it does not cause pain and if you do not suspect broken bones.

Direct pressure is better than a pressure point or a tourniquet, because direct pressure stops circulation only at the wound.

## Pressure Points

If you use a pressure point, keep using direct pressure (and elevation, when suitable). Add the pressure point.

Do not use a pressure point for an arm or leg wound unless direct pressure and elevation do not stop the bleeding. When bleeding is under control, gradually release the pressure point. Keep direct pressure on the wound, then bandage into place the cloths that were used to stop the bleeding.

Follow these steps for a wound that is not on an arm or leg:

1) Stop the bleeding with direct pressure.

2) Bandage into place the cloths used to stop the bleeding.

3) Give care to prevent shock.

4) Get medical care.

## When to Clean Wounds

If a wound is large, deep, or has been bleeding heavily, do not remove the cloths that were used to stop the bleeding.  <u>Do not</u> clean a serious wound that has finally stopped bleeding—it may start to bleed again.  Serious wounds should be cleaned only by trained medical personnel.

Clean a small wound with ordinary mild hand soap or mild detergent.  First wash your own hands, then wash the wound.  Rinse it thoroughly with clean water.  Put a clean, dry dressing and bandage on the wound.

53. A pad used to stop bleeding should be

[X] a. thick.
[ ] b. thin.


54. If elevation does <u>not</u> cause pain, elevate wounds on the arms and legs,

[X] a. even if the victim has unsplinted fractures.
[X] b. only if the victim does not have unsplinted fractures.


55. What method is best and is used <u>first</u> for stopping bleeding?

[ ] a. Tourniquet.
[X] b. Direct pressure (and elevation).
[ ] c. Pressure points.

112

Answers:

53.   a.  A pad used to stop bleeding should be <u>thick</u>.

54.   b.  Elevate a wound only if it does not cause pain and there are no suspected unsplinted fractures.

55.   b.  Use <u>direct pressure</u> and <u>elevation</u> first.

56.  If you cannot get a pad right away, stop severe bleeding with

[ ]   a.  a pressure point.
[x]   b.  your bare hand.

57.  Which picture shows
     how to squeeze the
     arm pressure point?

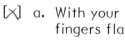

[x]  a.  With your
         fingers flat.

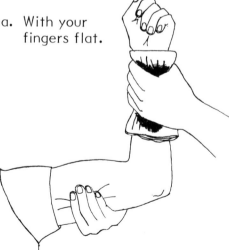

[ ]  b.  With your
         fingertips
         digging in.

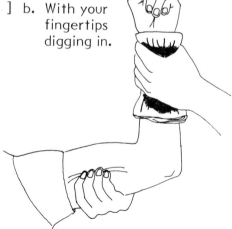

Answers:

56.   b. Stop severe bleeding <u>with your bare hand</u> if you cannot
         get a pad right away.


57.   a. Squeeze the arm pressure point with
         your fingers flat.

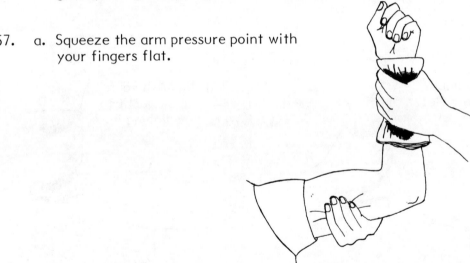

58. In this picture, which circle shows the location of a leg pressure point?

[λ]  a.
[ ]  b.

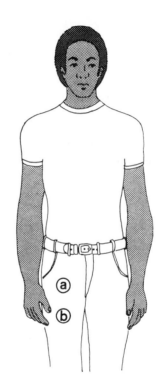

59. If you use a pressure point,

[ ]  a. do not apply direct pressure.
[x]  b. keep applying direct pressure.

116

Answers:

58.   a.  The leg pressure point is at circle a.

59.   b.  Keep applying direct pressure
          if you use a pressure point.

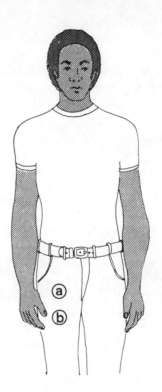

## Tourniquet

When you use a tourniquet, you risk sacrifice of a limb in order to save a life. The only time when there is not this risk is when the accident has amputated part of a limb and the tourniquet is tied right above the wound.

If you have decided to use a tourniquet, make it tight enough to stop all bleeding. A loose tourniquet will restrict the flow of blood in the veins without stopping the flow of blood in the arteries. This will cause _more_ blood loss, because the blood will pass into the wounded area through the arteries but will not return to the heart through the veins.

## Nosebleed

To stop a nosebleed, apply direct pressure by firmly pinching both nostrils shut with a thumb and forefinger. The victim should sit down and lean slightly forward, not backward. Leaning back or tipping the head back will cause blood to run down the throat and make the victim feel ill. The victim is usually able to pinch his or her own nose.

Keep pinching until the bleeding stops. If bleeding does not stop, you may have to pack the bleeding nostril lightly with gauze and squeeze again. (Do not use cotton. Cotton will get stuck.) Get medical help for frequent nosebleeds and nosebleeds that will not stop.

60. What method of controlling bleeding is so dangerous
that you should use it only if nothing else works?

[X] a. Tourniquet.
[ ] b. Pressure point.
[ ] c. Direct pressure.


61. Direct pressure will control bleeding in

[X] a. almost all cases.
[ ] b. only a few cases.

120

Answers:

60.   a.  A <u>tourniquet</u> is so dangerous that you should use it only if nothing else works.

61.   a.  Direct pressure will control bleeding in <u>almost all cases</u>.

*     *     *

Continue in the workbook with the lesson on shock.

# SHOCK

During your first thorough examination of the victim, after giving urgent care, give care to prevent shock. This kind of shock is not an electric shock. Shock can happen to anyone who is badly hurt or who has lost a lot of blood or other body fluid.

Shock depresses the body functions and can keep the heart, lungs, and other organs from working normally. It can be made worse by extreme pain and fright. Even if injuries do not directly cause death, the victim can go into shock and die. Anyone with a serious injury must have medical care—even if he or she seems to have recovered.

A trained medical person can treat shock by giving fluids directly into the blood vessels (intravenous fluids) to replace body fluids lost through an injury or illness. A first aider cannot do this, but he or she can give care that will help prevent shock.

Do your best to comfort, quiet, and soothe the victim. Keep him or her lying down, comfortable, and a normal temperature. If it is hot, provide shade; if it is cold, provide protection from cold both under and over the victim.

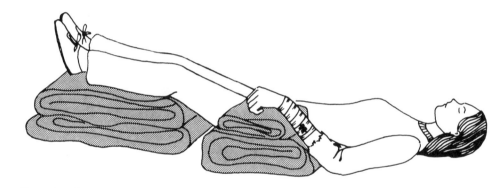

<u>Standard position</u> for giving care for shock: feet up, injury elevated. Do not elevate the injury if a broken bone is suspected. Do not elevate <u>any</u> unsplinted fractures.

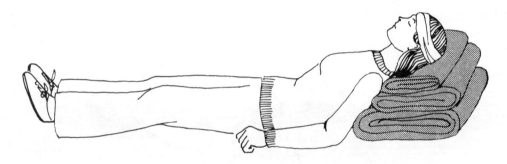

If the victim has a head wound or is having trouble breathing, elevate the

head and shoulders.  Do not elevate the feet and the head at the same time.

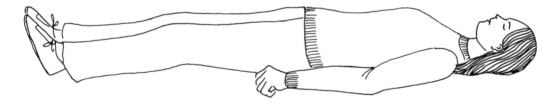

The victim should be flat on the back if fractures are suspected and not splinted,

if elevation is painful, or if you are unsure about which position is correct.

A victim who is bleeding from the mouth, vomiting, or may vomit should lie on one side, so fluid will drain from the mouth.

62. How do you position someone who is having trouble breathing?

[ ] a.

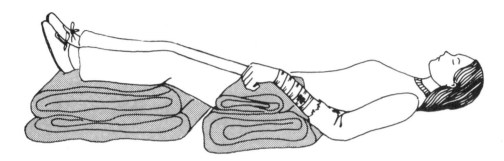

[X] b.

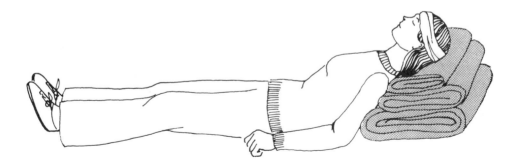

Answer:

62. b. A person who is having trouble breathing should have the head and shoulders up.

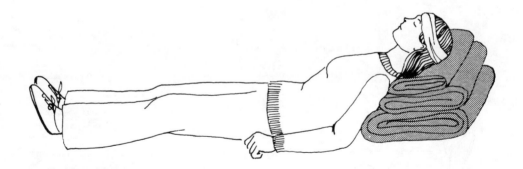

63. How do you position someone who is bleeding from the mouth?

[X] a.

[ ] b.

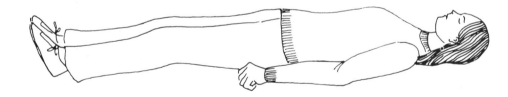

Answer:

63.  a.  A person who is bleeding from the mouth should lie <u>on one side</u> so fluid
     will not block the airway.

64. How do you position someone with unsplinted fractures?

[X] a.

[ ] b.

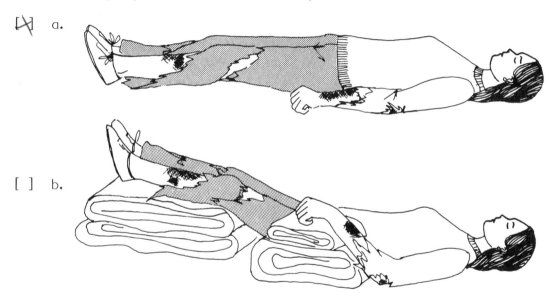

132

Answer:

64.  a.  A person with unsplinted fractures should lie <u>flat on the back</u>.

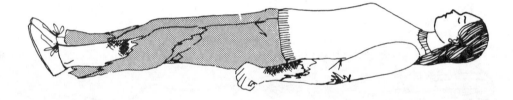

65. Which position is best for someone who is in shock?

[X] a.                    [ ] b.                    [ ] c.

66. Which is best for someone who has been vomiting or is bleeding from the mouth?

[ ] a.                    [ ] b.                    [X] c.

134

Answers:

65.   a.   This position is best for someone who is in shock:

66.   c.   This is best for someone who has been vomiting
           or is bleeding from the mouth:

67. Which is best for someone who is having trouble breathing?

[ ]  a.               [X]  b.               [ ]  c.

68. Which is best if elevation hurts the victim?

[ ]  a.               [ ]  b.               [X]  c.

136

Answers:

67.   b.   This is best for someone who is having trouble breathing:

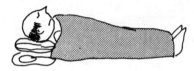

68.   c.   This is best if elevation hurts the victim:

*     *     *

Now you will have a break.

When you return, continue with Unit 2 in the workbook.

# UNIT 2

## POISONING

Poisoning is a more or less likely cause of sudden collapse, depending upon the situation in which you find the person.  Vomiting and heavy, labored breathing may indicate poisoning.  So may a deep sleep from which the victim cannot be aroused or eye pupils that are very large or very small.  These signs may also indicate disease, internal injuries, or other problems.  Look for a container that can tell you what the victim may have eaten or drunk.

Check around the mouth for signs of chemical burns.  Smell the breath.  Suspect poisoning if there are burns around the mouth, or if the breath smells very strong like gasoline.

If the victim is conscious, <u>first</u>
dilute any poison with water or milk.
Give one glass to an adult and
somewhat less to a child.

As soon as you have given water or milk and tried quickly to identify the poison, call the poison control center or a doctor.  If you cannot reach either one, call your city's emergency number or a hospital emergency number.  Say, "I have a poisoning emergency," so that you will be talking to the correct person.  Then say:

— What is wrong.

— Who you are.

— Where the victim is.

— Age and condition of the victim.

— What the victim was poisoned by (if known) and how much poison was taken (if known).

— What you have done.

DO NOT HANG UP THE TELEPHONE FIRST.

140

It is best to call a poison center, because they have current information on what to do for many poisons.  They will tell you whether or not to make the victim vomit, and they will tell you what else to do for the victim.

The directions for antidotes on many poison containers are <u>not</u> correct, so do not give anything but water or milk unless a poison center or doctor tells you to.  Some incorrect treatments can cause more damage than the poison itself!  A poison center will have the most up-to-date advice.

Find out from your instructor the nearest poison center number.  Call it in an emergency, even if it is a long-distance call.  Keep syrup of ipecac, activated charcoal, and epsom salts on hand.  The poison center may want you to use one or more of these.

The steps for a <u>conscious</u> victim of poisoning are:

<u>First</u>:   Dilute the poison by giving water or milk to drink.

<u>Then</u>:   Try quickly to identify the poison, but do not waste time.

          Call the poison center, hospital, or doctor.

          Give care to prevent shock.

If the person is unconscious or in convulsions, do not give water or milk. <u>Never</u>
give an unconscious person something to drink. Keep checking breathing. Try to identify
the poison and call for advice right away. Have the person lie on one side, so that
fluids such as vomit will not block the airway.

1.  What is the first step for a <u>conscious</u> victim of poisoning?

[ ]  a. Call the poison center.
[X]  b. Give water or milk to drink.
[ ]  c. Cause vomiting.


2.  What do you do right away for an <u>unconscious</u> victim of poisoning?

[X]  a. Check breathing and call the poison center.
[ ]  b. Give water or milk to drink.
[ ]  c. Cause vomiting.

144

Answers:

1.    b.   The first step for a <u>conscious</u> victim of poisoning is <u>give water or milk to drink</u>.

2.    a.   <u>Check breathing</u> and <u>call the poison center</u>. Do not give the victim anything to drink. Do not cause vomiting.

If you cannot get advice from a poison center or doctor right away, and the victim is conscious, you must decide whether to make the victim vomit.  Right after giving water or milk to drink, make the victim vomit these poisons:

     — Too much medicine or the wrong medicine.

     — Pest poisons.  These include bug and rat poison and weed killers.

To make the victim vomit, tickle the back of the throat with your finger or give syrup of ipecac, following directions on the container.

Some poisons should <u>not</u> be vomited.  Signs that tell you <u>not</u> to cause vomiting

are:

- Burns around the lips or mouth.  Poisons that burn the mouth
  and throat, such as drain cleaners and toilet cleaners, should
  not be vomited.  These are strong alkalis and acids.

- Breath odor like kerosene or gasoline.  Petroleum products
  should not be vomited.

Do not cause vomiting if you are not certain that you should.  Do not cause vomiting if the victim is unconscious, exhausted, or having convulsions.  Make sure the victim keeps breathing, give care to prevent shock, and get medical help as soon as possible.

149

3. Which of these poisons may cause burns in the mouth and throat?

[ ] a. Aspirin.
[x] b. Kerosene.
[x] c. Drain cleaner.

4. Check each step that applies to both conscious and unconscious victims, then check each step that applies only to conscious victims:

|  | Both Conscious and Unconscious Victims | Only Conscious Victims |
|---|---|---|
| a. Give water or milk. | [ ] | [x] |
| b. Try to identify poison. | [x] | [ ] |
| c. Call poison center. | [x] | [ ] |
| d. Treat for shock. | [x] | [ ] |
| e. Keep checking for breathing. | [x] | [ ] |

5. If you can contact a poison control center, should you try to decide whether the victim should vomit a poison?

[ ] a. Yes.
[x] b. No.

Answers:

3.  c. <u>Drain cleaner</u> may cause burns in the mouth and throat.

4.

|  | Both Conscious and Unconscious Victims | Only Conscious Victims |
|---|---|---|
| a. Give water or milk. | [ ] | [X] |
| b. Try to identify poison. | [X] | [ ] |
| c. Call poison center. | [X] | [ ] |
| d. Treat for shock. | [X] | [ ] |
| e. Keep checking for breathing. | [X] | [ ] |

5.  b. <u>No</u>. Call the poison center for advice.

Pest poisons, such as bug poison and weed killer, can poison a person not only if swallowed, but also if absorbed into the body through the skin.  If any pest poisons are spilled, dusted, or misted onto the skin or clothing, wash them off immediately.  If you become ill after being exposed to such products, get medical care or call a poison center for advice.

Small children are often poisoned because they put in their mouths almost everything they pick up. Put poisons, medicines, and household cleaners high in a cupboard that small children cannot open even if they climb up. If you have to put a poison in a new box or jar, put on a large label: <u>POISON</u> and what the poison is. Do not leave any poisons, even with labels, around children who can not read.

Many plants, fruits, and berries are poisonous. Do not eat a part of any plant unless you are sure it is safe.

6.   If bug poison or weed killer gets on your skin,

[X]  a.  wash it off immediately.
[ ]  b.  rub it off with your hand.


7.   If you feel ill after being exposed to bug poison or weed killer,

[ ]  a.  drink plenty of fluids and rest in bed.
[X]  b.  get medical help.

154

Answers:

6.  a. <u>Wash</u> bug poison or weed killer off your skin immediately.

7.  b. <u>Get medical help</u> if you feel ill after being exposed to bug
       poison or weed killer.

*    *    *

Continue in the workbook with the lesson on burns.

# BURNS

## Severity of Burns

The severity of a burn is determined by three factors:

- <u>Depth</u> of the burn.  This is called "degree".  First-degree burns are mild, second-degree burns are deeper, and third-degree burns are the deepest.

- <u>Size</u> or extent of the burn.  A very large burn is one that covers, for example, one side of the upper or lower half of an arm or leg, or the upper or lower back.

- <u>Location</u> of the burn.  Burns on critical areas of the body are especially dangerous.  The four critical areas are the hands, feet, face, and genital organs.

<u>Degree</u> tells only about depth—not about size or location.  The severity of a burn depends upon how deep the burn is, and how much of the body it covers, and where on the body it is located.

In addition to depth, size, and location, the age and physical condition of the victim can contribute to the seriousness of burns.  Victims who are very young, elderly, or ill are at greater risk from burns.

There is danger of infection in any burn, especially if there are blisters or loss of skin.  Any burn that seems to become infected must receive medical care as soon as possible.

Burns on the face, nose, or mouth may indicate burns in the breathing passages. Such burns can cause the airway to swell and keep the person from breathing.  Keep checking breathing, give mouth-to-mouth breathing if necessary, and get immediate medical help.

8.  The severity of a burn depends upon

[X]  a. depth, size, and location.
[ ]  b. depth and size, but not location.
[ ]  c. size and location, but not depth.


9.  What are the four critical areas of the body?

[ ]  a. Hands, feet, arms, and legs.
[X]  b. Hands, feet, face, and genitals.
[ ]  c. Feet, legs, genitals, and torso.


10.  If a person has burns on the face, be alert for injury to the

<u>breathing</u>  <u>passages</u>

Answers:

8.    a.  Severity of a burn depends upon <u>depth, size, and location</u>.

9.    b.  <u>Hands, feet, face, and genitals</u> are the four critical areas of the body.

10.   If a person has burns on the face, be alert for injury to the <u>breathing passages</u>.

11.  The danger of infection in a severely burned area is

[ ]  a.  very low.
[ ]  b.  moderate.
[X]  c.  very high.


12.  If a burn becomes infected, medical care is required

[ ]  a.  within a week.
[X]  b.  as soon as possible.

Answers:

11.   c.  The danger of infection in a severely burned area is <u>very high</u>.

12.   b.  An infected burn requires medical care <u>as soon as possible</u>.

## Thin Burns

A first-degree burn is not very deep. It involves only the surface layers of the skin. A second-degree burn goes deeper into the underlayers of the skin.

A mild first-degree burn on a person with light skin is pink or reddish—a mild sunburn, for example. On a person with dark skin, the color of a mild burn might not show. There are few or no blisters and little or no swelling.

A thin second-degree burn looks almost like a first-degree burn.  There are some small blisters, but blisters do not cover the entire burn.  A thin second-degree burn hurts and swells more than a first-degree burn, but there is not much swelling, and no skin is charred or burned away.  Check after 2 or 3 hours to be sure that a burn you thought was thin has not developed signs of being more serious.  Swelling and blistering are sometimes delayed.

Medical care may be needed to reduce pain from a second-degree burn when the burn might not otherwise seem serious enough to need it.

163

13. "Degree" refers to

[ ] a. depth, size, and location.
[X] b. depth only.


14. A first-degree burn has

[X] a. few or no blisters.
[ ] b. extensive, large blisters.


15. A thin second-degree burn has

[X] a. some small blisters.
[ ] b. extensive, large blisters.

Answers:

13.   b.  "Degree" refers only to <u>depth</u>.

14.   a.  A first-degree burn has <u>few or no blisters</u>.

15.   a.  A thin second-degree burn has <u>some small blisters</u>.

## Deep Burns

Deep burns cause a moderate to large amount of swelling.

A <u>moderately</u> deep second-degree burn may have large blisters or skin that peels away, leaving a small amount of raw, red area underneath.

A <u>deep</u> second-degree burn will have large blisters and some skin may be burned away. If the burn is open, it will ooze clear body fluids, giving it a wet surface.

A <u>third</u>-degree burn goes all the way through the skin. It may involve bone, muscle, and other tissue beneath the skin. A third-degree burn may be red and raw with ashy white or black charred areas. However, it may not be possible to tell a third-degree burn from a second-degree burn. Third-degree burns destroy nerve endings and flesh, so a third-degree burn may hurt less than a second-degree burn. Absence of pain does not mean that a burn is mild.

## Medical Care

Third-degree burns will not heal properly without medical care, and third-degree burns larger than about 4 centimeters (1 1/2 inches) in diameter will need skin grafts. All third-degree burns need medical care.

All large second-degree burns, and all second-degree burns on critical areas, no matter what size, need medical care.

Anyone who is burned may have some areas of first-degree burn and other areas of second-degree and third-degree burn. Base your decisions about first aid and medical care on the worst burns.

16. What type of burn may look raw and red, or ashy white, or charred?

[ ] a. First degree and thin second degree.
[X] b. Moderately deep second degree and deeper.


17. Does pain always indicate the severity of a burn?

[ ] a. Yes, the worse the burn, the greater the pain.
[X] b. No, third-degree burns are sometimes less painful than thinner burns because nerve endings are destroyed.


18. What advice would you give to a person who has a burn that does not heal?

[ ] a. Be patient. It takes a long time for burns to heal.
[X] b. Get medical care. Third-degree burns will not heal properly without medical care.

168

Answers:

16.  b.  <u>A moderately deep second-degree or deeper burn</u> may look raw and red, or ashy white, or charred.

17.  b.  <u>No</u>, third-degree burns are sometimes less painful than thinner burns because the nerve endings are destroyed.

18.  b.  <u>Get medical care.</u>  Third-degree burns will not heal properly without medical care.

19. What are the four critical areas of the body?

    a. _face_

    b. _feet_

    c. _hands_

    d. _genital areas_

20. What type of burn on a critical area requires immediate medical care?

[X] a. Second degree (and deeper).
[ ] b. Only third degree.

21. If a burn has a large number of blisters and some loss of skin, it is

[X] a. worse than thin second degree.
[ ] b. thin second degree.
[ ] c. first degree.

Answers:

19.  The four critical areas are

  a. <u>hands</u>
  b. <u>feet</u>
  c. <u>face</u>
  d. <u>genitals</u>

20.  a. <u>Second-degree and deeper</u> burns on critical areas require
       immediate medical care.

21.  a. A burn is <u>worse than thin second degree</u> if it has a large number of
       blisters and some loss of skin.

22. A second-degree burn on the entire front of the thigh of a young adult is

[X] a. serious.
[ ] b. not serious.


23. A small second-degree burn on the back of an infant is

[X] a. serious.
[X] b. not serious.


24. What three factors determine the severity of a burn?

a. ___depth___
b. ___location___
c. ___size___

Answers:

22.   a.  Any large second-degree burn is <u>serious</u>.

23.   a.  Any second-degree burn on the back of an infant is <u>serious</u>.

24.   The severity of a burn is determined by

a.  <u>depth</u>
b.  <u>size</u>
c.  <u>location</u>

25. Which deep second-degree and third-degree burns should receive immediate medical attention?

☒ a. All.
[ ] b. Only those on very young people, elderly people, and sick people.

26. You think a burn caused by hot grease may be as deep as a third-degree burn, but you cannot tell for sure. You should assume that it is a

[ ] a. second-degree burn.
☒ b. third-degree burn.

Answers:

25.  a.  <u>All</u> deep second-degree and third-degree burns should receive
         immediate medical attention.


26.  b.  Assume that it is a <u>third-degree</u> burn.  Give or obtain treatment for
         the most serious burn it <u>could</u> be.

## First Aid for Heat Burns

The three major objectives of first aid for heat burns are to relieve pain, to reduce the chance of infection by preventing contamination, and to reduce the likelihood of shock.

Cooling will reduce the pain of a burn. Aspirin may be given to a conscious person who has mild burns, if the person is not allergic to aspirin. Pain requiring stronger medication should be treated by a doctor.

**Small, Thin Burns**.  Cool water can be used directly on a small burn that is not open and not very deep.  Put cool water on the burn right away.  Immerse it if possible.  Do not add anything to the water.  Cool the burn until pain is reduced.  Then gently pat the area dry with sterile gauze.

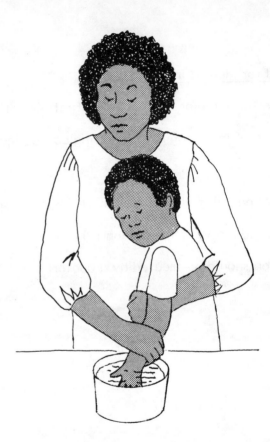

A small, thin burn does not need to be bandaged unless there are open areas or blisters that need protection.  If necessary, cover the burn with a dry, sterile dressing.  Hold the dressing in place with a bandage or tape.  You may leave the dressing on the burn for a day or two, or change it more often, as it suits the victim.

Large, Thin Burns.  Cool a large, thin burn with water immediately and until pain subsides.  Dry it gently and cover it with a thick, dry, sterile dressing.  Dry, insulated cold packs may be used over the dressing if they make the victim more comfortable.

178

Deep Burns.  Most moderate second-degree and deeper burns have open areas where blisters break or skin is burned away.  Do not put water directly on an open burn to cool it.  Water increases the danger of infection in open burns.  Instead, cover the burn with a thick, dry, sterile dressing and bandage.  If burned clothing is sticking to a burn, place the dressing right over it.  Do not remove clothing that is sticking to a burn.

Dry, insulated cold packs may be used over a dressing on small areas such as the face, hands, and feet.  Do not wet the dressing.  Do not use cold packs if their weight causes pain.

## Care to Prevent Shock

Have the victim lie down, elevate burned areas if elevation does not cause pain or further injury, maintain a normal body temperature, and get medical care.

The major cause of shock in burn victims is massive loss of body fluid through the burned area. Water may be given by mouth to someone who has thin burns or a small, deep burn. Do not give fruit juices or alcoholic beverages to a burn victim. A victim with large, deep burns must be given special treatment by medical personnel.

## Cautions

- Do not put anything oily or salty, such as butter, on a burn. Salt makes a burn hurt worse and draws more fluid out of the burned tissue. Anything oily will have to be removed from a burn before medical treatment can be given.

- Do not use water directly on heat burns to cool them if the skin is blistered or broken.

- In order to heal properly, burns should not be rubbed by clothing or bandages. No burn should bear weight.

- Medical personnel who are caring for the victim of severe burns should change dressings and bandages.

## Heat Burns of the Eye

Heat burns of the eye can be caused by a splash of hot grease or a hot cinder from an open fire. Gently <u>flood</u> water into any eye burn except a very deep burn caused by heat. Then examine the eye. If a cinder or other object is loose on the surface of the eye, gently touch it out with the corner of a clean handkerchief or sterile bandage.

Cover the eye with a thick, dry, sterile dressing, and bandage the dressing in place. Tell the person not to rub the eye. If a cinder or any other object cannot be removed or is embedded in the eye, keep the eye from moving by bandaging both eyes. If possible, bandage both eyes for any eye burn or injury.

Treat deep eye burns caused by heat as third-degree burns: <u>do</u> <u>not</u> flood the eye with water. Bandage both eyes, put a cold pack over the bandage on the injured eye, elevate the head and shoulders, and give care to prevent shock.

Immediate medical care is needed for any burn of the eye and for any object embedded in the eye. If possible, get care from an eye doctor (opthalmologist).

27. If charred clothing is sticking to a burn, the clothing should be

[ ] a. removed before you bandage the burn.
[X] b. left on the burn when you bandage it.


28. One way to relieve the pain of a small, deep burn is to

[X] a. cool it with cold packs.
[ ] b. warm it with hot packs.


29. If you put a burn in water, should you add anything to the water?

[ ] a. Yes.
[X] b. No.

184

Answers:

27.  b.  <u>Bandage over clothing</u> that is sticking to a burn.

28.  a.  Relieve the pain with <u>cold packs</u>.

29.  b.  <u>No</u>, do not add anything to the water.

185

30.   Do you put water into deep heat burns of the eye?

[ ]   a. Yes.
[x]   b. No.


31.   Which burns may be cooled directly in water?

[x]   a. Small, thin burns with no open tissue.
[ ]   b. Large, deep burns with open tissue.

186

Answers:

30.   b.  <u>No</u>, do not use water in any deep heat burns.

31.   a.  <u>Small, thin burns</u> with no open tissue may be cooled directly in water.

## First Aid for Chemical Burns of the Skin

If a strong chemical gets on skin, wash it off quickly. It may cause burns or an allergic reaction, or it may be absorbed through the skin. Wash chemical burns of <u>all</u> <u>thicknesses</u>. Don't scrub or use soap—just flood the burn with running water. Pour water on it if there is no running water. Wash for at least <u>5</u> minutes. Use lots of water.

Take off all clothing on which a chemical has spilled, including clothing that is touching a burn.

Note how care for chemical burns is different from care for heat burns: wash <u>all</u> chemical burns, and remove clothing from <u>all</u> chemical burns. Followup care for chemical burns is the same as for heat burns.

Call a poison control center to find out if there are other steps you can take. But wash the chemical off first, before you call. Some product labels tell how to neutralize chemicals, but these directions may be wrong. Do not try to neutralize a chemical with another chemical unless a poison center or doctor tells you what to do.

After you have washed the chemical off, cover the burn with a thick, dry, sterile dressing and bandage, give care for shock, and get medical help immediately.

32.    Remove clothing from a burn that was caused by

[X]   a.  chemicals.
[ ]   b.  fire or heat.


33.    Wash a chemical burn

[ ]   a.  only if it is <u>not</u> deep and open.
[X]   b.  even if it <u>is</u> deep and open.


34.    What do you do first for a chemical burn?

[X]   a.  Wash the chemical off for at least 5 minutes.
[ ]   b.  Neutralize the chemical, then wash it off for at least 5 minutes.

Answers:

32.   a.   <u>Remove clothing from a chemical burn</u> to help get rid of the chemical.

33.   b.   Wash a chemical burn <u>even if it is deep and open</u>.

34.   a.   First <u>wash</u> the chemical off for at least <u>5 minutes</u>.

## Chemical Burns of the Eye

If someone gets a chemical in an eye, put the eye under gently running water that is neither very hot nor very cold as soon as possible. Have the victim hold the eyelids open, or hold them open with your fingers, so the water will run into the eye.

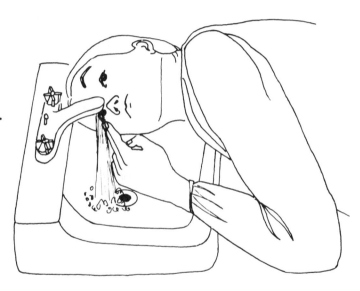

Have the victim remove contact lenses while water is being obtained or is first run into the eye.  Do not delay washing the eye, but remove the lens as soon as possible.

Run water from the inside to the outside of the eye, with the burned eye nearer to the floor, so that the chemical is not washed into the other eye.  Some chemicals keep burning for a long time and are difficult to remove, so wash the eye for about 15 minutes.  After you have washed the eye, examine it carefully.  If you see any loose specks of chemical on the eye, gently lift them off with gauze or clean cloth.

Cover the eye with a dry, sterile dressing.  If possible, help keep the burned or injured eye from moving by bandaging both eyes.  Get immediate medical care.

35.  Wash a chemical out of an eye for at least

[ ]   a.  1 minute.
[ ]   b.  5 minutes.
[X]   c.  15 minutes.


36.  Wash a chemical off the skin for at least

[ ]   a.  1 minute.
[X]   b.  5 minutes.
[ ]   c.  15 minutes.

194

Answers:

35.   c.  Wash a chemical out of an eye for at least <u>15 minutes</u>.


36.   b.  Wash a chemical off the skin for at least <u>5 minutes</u>.

37. If a person with chemical in an eye is wearing contact lenses,

[ ]  a. remove the lens right away; delay washing until you are
        sure it is out of the burned eye.
[X]  b. remove the lens right away, but do not delay starting to
        run water in the eye.


38. While chemical is being washed from an eye,

[X]  a. keep the eye open, even if you have to hold it open with your fingers.
[ ]  b. tell the victim to keep the eye open unless it hurts to much.

Answers:

37.   b.   Remove the lens <u>right away</u>, but <u>do not delay</u> starting
            to run water in the eye.


38.   a.   <u>Keep the eye open</u>, even if you have to hold it open with your fingers.

Many drugs and chemicals are used in spray form. None of these should be sprayed in the eyes or inhaled into the lungs. If something is sprayed into the eyes, first aid is the same as for any other chemical burn of the eye: wash it all out.

## Prevention of Burns

Many fires and burns result from carelessness with cigarettes, matches, electricity, and gasoline. Be careful when working around electrical wiring, such as when pruning trees where branches may fall on wires, and when working on the roof of a building. Do not pour gasoline from one container to another when you are in an enclosed space, such as a shed or garage. Do not pour gasoline near a hot engine, such as a chain saw or lawn mower. Do not add charcoal lighting fluid to a smouldering fire.

Most chemical burns can be avoided by following warnings on labels. Handle strong chemicals carefully and keep them away from children.

\*      \*      \*

Now you will see the films on bandaging.

# HEAD INJURIES, INTERNAL INJURIES, AND GUNSHOT WOUNDS

## Examine the Victim

Carefully examine the victim for injuries and for other conditions that may not be as obvious as severe bleeding or stopped breathing. In some emergencies you will examine the victim right away; in others you will first give urgent care and then examine the victim more carefully.

Start at the head and work toward the feet. Look for anything that does not seem normal. Is the victim awake? In a daze? Unconscious? Are there lumps, bumps, bruises, cuts, deformed body parts, or other signs of injury? The victim may be able to tell you what happened or where it hurts. Bystanders may also be able to tell you what happened.

Head Injury

Some signs of head injury are:

- Bumps, bruises, or cuts on the head.

- Headache.

- Dizziness.

- Unconsciousness (immediate or delayed half an hour or more).

- The pupil of one eye larger than the other.

- Sleepiness or inability to be wakened.

- Bleeding or fluid draining from the mouth, nose, or ears.

- Facial muscles or other body parts paralyzed or working abnormally.

It is sometimes hard to decide if there has been a head injury. Any or all of the signs may be present <u>or absent</u> in a victim of a head injury.

Whenever an accident involves force (a fall, an automobile accident, a blow to the head) or a person suffers unconsciousness, headache, or dizziness after an accident, there may be a head injury.

Unconsciousness and extreme sleepiness signal more-serious head injuries, but if any of the signs are present within a few minutes to a few days after an accident, get medical care immediately.

Keep an injured head, neck, or spine from moving, bending, or twisting.  A person with head injuries that you can see may also have neck and spine injuries that you cannot see.  A victim with such injuries must be tied to a backboard for transportation.  Persons with neck or spine injuries must be moved as a unit, in a straight line—not one part at a time.  If you are not trained to use a backboard, do not move the victim if you suspect such injuries.

First aid for a head injury or suspected head injury is:

- Keep the victim lying flat or, if you are quite sure there is no injury to the neck or back, with the head and shoulders raised slightly. Do not raise the feet.

- Watch carefully for stopped breathing.

- Get medical help immediately.

- Do not give stimulants, alcohol, or other fluids to drink.

If transportation is necessary, handle the victim very gently.

An unconscious victim should lie on one side so that fluids can drain from the mouth.  Check breathing of an unconscious person <u>often</u>.

39. How can you keep fluids from blocking the airway of an unconscious person?

[ ] a. Place the person on the back with the feet raised.
[✓] b. Place the person on one side.

40. How should you treat a victim of head injury?

[✓] a. Gently, with as little movement as possible.
[ ] b. Carefully help the victim to sit up.

41. A boy slips at the edge of a swimming pool and falls backward onto the wet sidewalk. He cannot move his legs. Should you move him to a dry place immediately?

[ ] a. Yes.
[✓] b. No.

Answers:

39.   b.  Place an unconscious person <u>on one side</u> to keep fluids from blocking
          the airway.

40.   a.  Treat a victim or head injury <u>gently, with as little movement as possible.</u>

41.   b.  <u>No.</u>  Do not move the victim unless you have to.

## Internal Injuries

Internal injuries may be caused by accidents involving force, and by penetrating wounds.

Signs of internal injury are pain and tenderness; faintness; nausea; vomiting or coughing up blood; blood in the urine or feces; cool, clammy skin; restlessness; thirst; and a rapid, weak pulse.

If _any_ internal injury is suspected, the person should lie down and not be moved without proper transportation in a lying position. Do not give fluids by mouth.

## Gunshot Wounds

The size of a gunshot wound on the surface does not indicate how serious the internal injuries are. Gunshot wounds often cause fractures in addition to other internal injuries. Examine the victim carefully. There may also be more bullet wounds or a wound on the opposite side where the bullet left the body.

If a lung is punctured, air will go in and out of the wound and the lung may collapse and stop working. Bandage the chest firmly to prevent this.

42. What do you do if you suspect a broken neck?
Keep the neck and spine from _moving_.

43. Can you always tell for sure if someone is hurt or bleeding inside?

[ ] a. Yes.
[X] b. No.

44. Even if there are no obvious injuries, the victim of a serious accident should lie down and be seen by a doctor. The victim may have

[ ] a. internal injuries or loss of appetite.
[X] b. internal injuries or may go into shock.
[ ] c. a history of heart disease or may go into shock.

Answers:

42.  Keep the neck and spine from <u>moving, bending, or twisting.</u>

43.  b.  <u>No</u>, you cannot always tell for sure.

44.  b.  The victim may have <u>internal injuries</u> or may go into <u>shock</u>.

45. Does the size of a gunshot wound on the surface tell you how serious the internal injuries are?

[ ] a. Yes.
[x] b. No.


46. If a person's chest is penetrated, you should bandage the wound firmly. Why?

[x] a. To keep air from going in and out through the wound.
[ ] b. To keep the person's chest from moving.

Answers:


45.   b.   <u>No</u>.  The size of a gunshot wound on the surface does not indicate how serious the internal injuries are.


46.   a.   Bandage the chest firmly to keep air from going in and out through the wound.


*   *   *


Now you will have a break.

When you return, continue with Unit 3 in the workbook.

# UNIT 3

## INJURIES OF THE EYE

### Foreign Object on the Surface of the Eye or Eyelid

Follow these steps to remove a speck of dirt from the outside of the eyeball or from the inside of the eyelid:

1) Keep the victim from rubbing the eye. Rubbing may push the object into the eye or eyelid and make removal more difficult.

2) Have the victim blink and try to make tears. The dirt may be loosened and swept away by tears.

3) Wash your hands thoroughly before examining the victim's eye.

4) Pull down the lower lid to see if the speck is on the inner surface of the lid. If so, lift it off gently with the corner of a clean handkerchief.

214

5)  If you cannot see the speck, it may be on the inside of the upper lid.  Have the victim look down.  Grasp the lashes of the upper lid gently between the thumb and forefinger and pull the lid out and down over the lower lid. This may dislodge the dirt.

6)  If the dirt is not yet removed, flush the eye with clean water, using an eye dropper or small bulb syringe.

If these steps do not work, put a clean dry dressing over the eye and bandage both eyes (if possible); get medical help.  Never try to use a solid object, such as a toothpick, to remove an object from the eye.

1.  If there is a speck resting on the surface of an eyelid, can you touch the speck with the corner of a clean handkerchief?

[X]  a.  Yes.
[ ]  b.  No.

2.  If there is a speck in the eye, should the victim blink to make tears?

[X]  a.  Yes.
[ ]  b.  No.

3.  Can you use clean water from an eyedropper to try to get a speck out of the eye?

[X]  a.  Yes.
[ ]  b.  No.

4.  Can you touch the surface of the eye with fingers or something like a match?

[ ]  a.  Yes.
[X]  b.  No.

Answers:

1.    a.  <u>Yes</u>, you can touch a speck on the eyelid with a clean handkerchief.

2.    a.  <u>Yes</u>, try to make tears to get a speck to float out of the eye.

3.    a.  <u>Yes</u>, try to float a speck gently out of the eye with clean water.

4.    b.  <u>No</u>, do not touch the surface of the eye with anything firm, hard, or unclean.

## Serious Injury of the Eye

The whole eye may be damaged in a serious injury; vision may be lost.  Put a dry, sterile or clean dressing over a seriously injured eye.  Cover both eyes to keep the injured eye from moving.

If an object is sticking in or embedded in the eye, do not try to remove the object or wash the eye.  Cover the eyes with a bandage but do not press on the object or the injured eye.

Call ahead to an eye specialist or take the victim to a hospital emergency room.  The victim should be transported lying down.  The sooner medical care is obtained, the greater the chances of saving the victim's sight.

## Injury of the Eyelid

A torn eyelid is serious and must be repaired immediately. Blindness will result from long exposure of the eye without an eyelid. If there is no dirt or object to get stuck in the eye, stop bleeding by gently applying direct pressure. Apply a sterile or clean dressing, and bandage it in place. Seek medical care without delay.

5. With serious injuries of the eyes, time in obtaining medical care

[X] a. is important, because a long time-delay can mean greater loss of vision.
[ ] b. is not too important, because the damage has already been done.

6. A torn eyelid

[ ] a. will heal by itself.
[X] b. needs immediate medical care.

7. What should you do if something seems to be embedded in an eye?

[ ] a. Try to lift the object out.
[X] b. Bandage both eyes and get medical care.

Answers:

5.    a.  A long time-delay can mean greater loss of vision.

6.    b.  A torn eyelid needs <u>immediate medical care</u>.

7.    b.  If something seems embedded in an eye, <u>get medical care</u>.

\*    \*    \*

Continue in the workbook with the lesson about infection, tetanus, and animal bites.

# INFECTION, TETANUS, AND ANIMAL BITES

## Infection

Infection is caused by growth of bacteria (germs) that get into tissues of the body.  A dangerous infection can develop even in a very minor wound.  Many wounds are contaminated by dirt and other foreign material and must be cleaned before they are allowed to heal.

Cleaning can greatly reduce the chance of infection.  However, you should clean only <u>small</u> wounds that have not been bleeding heavily.

Clean a small wound with ordinary mild hand soap or mild detergent. First wash your own hands, then wash in and around the wound. Rinse thoroughly with clean water —running tap water is best. Remove small, slightly embedded objects, such as gravel in abrasions. Blot—do not rub—the wound dry with sterile gauze or clean cloth. Do not use fluffy or fuzzy material such as loose cotton; it may stick in the wound. Cover the wound with a clean, dry dressing that is slightly larger than the wound, so that dirt cannot get into open tissue.

Do not clean a serious wound—it may start to bleed again. If a wound is large, deep, or has been bleeding heavily, leave the compress in place. Serious wounds should be cleaned only by trained medical personnel.

Infection can start in a wound within hours or days.  Get medical help immediately if any of these signs develop:

- Pain or tenderness at the wound.

- Redness, heat, or swelling at the wound.

- Pus collected beneath the skin or in the wound.

- Red streaks leading from the wound, showing that infection is spreading.

- Swollen lymph glands in the groin (leg infection), in an armpit (arm infection), or in the neck (infection of the neck or head).

An infection in a wound may also cause general signs of illness:  fever (high body temperature), nausea, headache, and feeling of illness.  Any of these should lead you to suspect infection, whether or not there are signs of infection at the wound itself.

Tetanus

Tetanus infection (lockjaw) is a serious reaction to the growth of a certain kind of bacteria in a wound. Tetanus can infect any open wound and can cause death.

Tetanus bacteria are more likely to infect puncture wounds and other wounds that involve tissues below the skin. Clean a puncture wound carefully, get a doctor's advice about the possible need for a tetanus shot, and watch for signs of infection.

8. What kinds of wounds should a first aider wash?

☒ a. Only small wounds.
[ ] b. All wounds.
[ ] c. Only large, dirty wounds.

9. Tetanus is most likely with which type of wound?

[ ] a. Abrasion.
☒ b. Puncture.
[ ] c. Incision.

10. Any open wound can become contaminated with tetanus bacteria.

☒ a. True.
[ ] b. False.

226

Answers:

8.  a. A first aider should wash <u>only small wounds</u>.

9.  b. Tetanus is most likely with <u>puncture</u> wounds.

10. a. <u>True</u>. Any open wound can become contaminated by tetanus bacteria. Tetanus is less likely to infect open wounds that bleed freely.

## Care for Infections

If any wound becomes infected, prompt medical care is needed. If there will be a delay in getting medical care, treat the infection this way:

1) Have the victim lie down and, if possible, elevate the infected part.

2) Keep both the victim and the infected area from moving.

3) Apply warm packs to the infected part, using hot water bottles (not burning hot) or warm, moist towels or cloths directly on the infection. You test the heat of anything before you put it on someone else, since a person with an injury may not be able to feel something that burns.

4) Apply the warm packs for 30 minutes—changing them to keep them warm. Then take the warm packs off and cover the wound with a clean, dry dressing to keep out air and absorb drainage for another 30 minutes. Continue to apply warm packs for 30 minutes, then a dry dressing for the next 30 minutes, until medical help can be obtained.

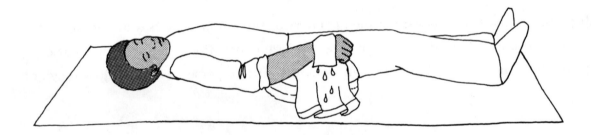

5) Keep track of the victim's temperature and the general appearance of the wound.

11.  If a wound becomes infected, have the victim

[X]  a.  lie down and remain inactive.
[ ]  b.  keep as active as possible.


12.  What should you do for an infection?

[X]  a.  Get prompt medical care; apply warm packs if there will be a delay
         in getting medical care.
[ ]  b.  Apply warm packs; get medical care if the infection seems to get worse.


13.  Warm, moist packs and dry dressings should be exchanged every

[ ]  a.  5 minutes.
[X]  b.  30 minutes.
[ ]  c.  2 hours.

Answers:

11.  a.  A person with an infection should <u>lie down and remain inactive</u>.

12.  a.  <u>Get prompt medical care</u>; apply heat if there will be a delay in getting medical care for an infection.

13.  b.  Exchange warm packs and dry dressings every <u>30 minutes</u>.

## Animal and Human Bites

An animal or human bite that breaks the skin will probably become infected if not given medical care. Wash the wound with soap and water. Flush it with running water if possible. Then cover it with a sterile dressing and get medical care. Tell the victim not to move the injured area more than necessary, until medical attention can be given.

A person who is bitten by an animal may become infected by tetanus or rabies.

Warm-blooded animals, such as dogs, cats, bats, rats, and squirrels, can transmit rabies. Rabies is transmitted when the saliva from an infected animal contacts an open wound (even a scratch) or any normal body opening, such as the mouth or eye. The infected animal can transmit rabies by biting or licking another animal or person.

After a person has been bitten by a rabid animal, there is a period of time while the disease develops. If the person receives immunization (a series of shots) soon enough after being bitten, rabies can be prevented.

There is no proved or widely available cure after rabies has developed. Most victims of rabies die once the final stages appear. For this reason you must find out right away if a bite was caused by a rabid animal.

Animals show varying signs of rabies. <u>The behavior of an animal with rabies may be unusual</u>. For example, a wild animal with rabies may not run away from you. An animal with rabies may be drooling, irritable, unusually active, or clearly dangerous. On the other hand, a rabid animal may be unusually quiet or loving. The animal may also be partly paralyzed.

An animal that bites someone must be watched by health personnel to find out if it has rabies. Catch it or restrain it, taking care not to be bitten. Do not kill the animal unless you have to. Avoid damaging the head. Get help from the police, a veterinarian, or local public health authority. They will know where and how long such an animal is to be kept and watched—usually for 15 days.

If you must kill an animal to keep it from getting away, preserve the head. Keep it in ice, if possible, but do not freeze it. Take it to a veterinarian who will examine the brain for signs of rabies.

14.   Before seeking medical care for an animal or human bite,

[X]   a.  wash the wound with soap and water; rinse; apply a dressing.
[ ]   b.  apply a dressing but do not wash the wound.


15.   If an animal bites someone, which is better to do?

[ ]   a.  Kill the animal; then take it to a veterinarian.
[X]   b.  Restrain the animal; have it examined by a veterinarian.

Answers:

14.  a.  <u>Wash, rinse, and apply a dressing</u> to an animal or human bite.

15.  b.  <u>Restrain</u> the animal and have it examined by a veterinarian.

*   *   *

Now you will see the films about splinting and care for fractures.

# FRACTURES, SPRAINS, AND STRAINS

Fractures and injuries to joints and muscles are caused most often by motor vehicle accidents and falls. Falls, many of which occur in the home, are a leading cause of accidental death for persons over 65 years of age.

## Closed and Open Fractures

A closed fracture is an injury beneath the skin and may be difficult to detect. To decide whether to suspect a fracture, find out what happened and what the victim thinks is wrong, and examine the victim carefully. Do not move or have the victim move body parts that may be injured. The signs of a closed fracture are pain, swelling, deformity, and discoloration.

An open fracture is a fracture associated with an open wound.  The wound is usually caused by a broken bone end that tears through the skin.  Sometimes a wound is caused by machinery or by a missile, such as a bullet, that penetrates the skin and breaks one or more bones.

Open fractures are generally much more serious than closed fractures because of the amount of tissue damage, bleeding, and danger of infection.  In most cases the bone slips back inside the skin again.  Do not try to push a bone end back.  This can only cause further serious injury.

If you cannot get medical help, splint fractures with as little movement of the bones as possible.  Do not try to reduce or straighten fractures, dislocations, or other deformities.

16. You think that a young woman has a broken wrist but a bystander says, "Don't worry, she's moving her fingers."  What should you do?

[ ]  a.  Help her stand up.
[x]  b.  Get her to stop moving her fingers.


17. You cannot tell whether a person's ankle is broken or sprained. You should assume it is

[ ]  a.  sprained.
[x]  b.  broken.

Answers:

16.  b.  Get her to stop moving her fingers.

17.  b.  If you are not certain, assume it is broken.

18. A man who has just been in an auto accident has a pain in his neck. His neck is not swollen or tender. What should you do?

[ ] a. Ask the victim if he can move his head.
[X] b. Have the victim remain quiet and not move.

19. Which fractures are the most difficult to identify?

[X] a. Closed.
[ ] b. Open.

Answers:

18.  b.  Have the victim remain quiet and not move.

19.  a.  <u>Closed</u> fractures are difficult to identify.

## Sprains and Strains

The ankles, fingers, wrists, and knees are most often sprained. Sprains are usually the result of forcing a limb beyond the normal range of a joint. The ligaments, tendons, and blood vessels are stretched or torn. The signs of a sprain are swelling, tenderness, pain on motion, and discoloration. It is usually impossible to tell a sprain from a closed fracture without an X-ray. Small chip fractures often accompany sprains.

Always immobilize a sprain as you would a fracture, and get medical help. Elevate the joint and put cold, wet cloths or an ice bag on it during the first half hour after the accident to retard swelling.

A strain is injury to muscles. The fibers are stretched or torn. Back strains are often caused by improper lifting. Lift with your legs, not your back. A person with a strain should rest and have warm, wet applications on the injured muscles. A person with a strained back should lie flat on the back on a hard surface, and obtain medical advice.

## Dislocations

A dislocation is a displacement of a bone end from a joint. Dislocations are usually caused by falls and blows. Fractures may accompany a dislocation. Unless given proper care, a dislocation may occur repeatedly.

The signs of a dislocation are similar to those of a closed fracture: swelling, tenderness to touch, deformity, pain, and discoloration.

Do not try to reduce a dislocation. Keep the part quiet and get medical care. Immobilize a dislocated shoulder with an arm sling during transportation.

20. How can you tell the difference between a closed fracture and a sprain?

[ ] a. You can tell by feeling the injured area.
[X] b. You cannot usually tell the difference.


21. How do you care for a strain?

[ ] a. Rest and mild exercise.
[ ] b. Warm, wet applications, and mild exercise.
[X] c. Rest, and warm, wet applications.

246

Answers:


20.   b.  You cannot usually tell the difference between a closed fracture
          and a sprain.  Medical advice is needed.


21.   c.  Rest and warm, wet applications are the first aid care for a strain.


\*     \*     \*


Continue with the workbook lesson on fainting, epilepsy,

and other sources of convulsions.

# FAINTING, EPILEPSY, AND OTHER SOURCES OF CONVULSIONS

## Fainting

Fainting happens when the blood supply to the brain is reduced for a short time. A person who feels faint should lie down with the head low. If lying down is not possible, the person should sit down, lower the head between the knees, and breathe deeply.

A person who has fainted will recover consciousness almost immediately. He or she should rest lying down for ten minutes or more until recovery is complete. If recovery is not immediate, get medical advice, because the case is not simple fainting. If fainting occurs frequently, get medical advice.

## Epilepsy and Other Sources of Convulsions

The two major signs of a serious epileptic attack are convulsions and loss of consciousness.  A mild attack may last only a second and not be noticed by others. A person with epilepsy is not crazy; he or she will not hurt you.

Epilepsy can usually be controlled by special medication.  The victim or someone close to the victim should know about this, or you should consult a doctor.

22. How can you tell the difference between fainting and a more serious condition?

[ ] a. In most cases you cannot tell the difference.
[x] b. A victim of fainting will recover almost immediately.

23. Check the <u>three</u> most important things to do for any victim of convulsions.

[ ] a. Give fluids to drink.
[x] b. Give mouth-to-mouth or mouth-to-nose breathing if necessary.
[x] c. Obtain medical care.
[ ] d. Recommend mild exercise.
[x] e. Keep the person from injury.

252

Answers:

22. b. A victim of fainting will recover almost immediately.

23. The three most important things to do for a victim of convulsions are checked:

[ ] a. Give fluids to drink.
[X] b. Give mouth-to-mouth or mouth-to-nose breathing if necessary.
[X] c. Obtain medical care.
[ ] d. Recommend mild exercise.
[X] e. Keep the person from injury.

*    *    *

Continue with the workbook lesson on ill effects of heat and cold.

# ILL EFFECTS OF HEAT AND COLD

## Heat Stroke and Heat Exhaustion

Heat stroke is always life-threatening. Heat exhaustion is a milder condition than heat stroke. Both conditions occur most often on hot days during physical activity. Anyone can have either condition, and either condition can happen to older people even during such mild activity as taking a walk.

In heat stroke, the person's temperature control system that causes sweating stops working correctly. The body temperature rises so high that brain damage and death will result if the person is not cooled quickly. The main signs of heat stroke are red or flushed skin; hot, dry skin, although the person may have been sweating earlier; and extremely high body temperature, often to 41°C (106°F). There may be dizziness, nausea, headache, rapid pulse, and unconsciousness.

Heat exhaustion is much less dangerous than heat stroke. The major signs of heat exhaustion are pale, clammy skin, profuse perspiration, and extreme tiredness or weakness. The body temperature is approximately normal. The person may have a headache and may vomit.

Here are the most important differences between the signs for heat stroke and heat exhaustion:

Heat stroke: skin hot and dry, and very high body temperature.

Heat exhaustion: skin cool and wet from sweating, and normal body temperature.

24. Which condition involves profuse sweating and normal body temperature?

[ ] a. Heat stroke.
[X] b. Heat exhaustion.


25. Which condition is <u>always</u> serious?

[X] a. Heat stroke.
[ ] b. Heat exhaustion.

Answers:

24.   b.  <u>Heat exhaustion</u> involves profuse sweating and normal body temperature.

25.   a.  <u>Heat stroke</u> is always serious.

26. What are the two important signs of heat stroke (the life-threatening condition)?

[X] a. Red or flushed, hot, dry skin, and high body temperature.
[ ] b. Pale skin, profuse sweating, and normal body temperature.

27. What are the two important signs of heat exhaustion (the milder condition)?

[ ] a. Red or flushed, hot, dry skin, and high body temperature.
[X] b. Pale skin, profuse sweating, and normal body temperature.

Answers:

26.   a.  Red or flushed, hot, dry skin and high body temperature
          are signs of heat stroke.


27.   b.  Pale skin, profuse sweating and normal body temperature
          are signs of heat exhaustion.

Cool a victim of heat stroke quickly. If the body temperature is not brought down fast, permanent brain damage or death will result. Soak the person in cool but not cold water, sponge the body with rubbing alcohol or cool water, or pour water on the body to reduce the temperature to a safe level—about 39°C (102°F). Then stop cooling and observe the victim for 10 minutes. If the temperature starts to rise again, cool the victim again. Do not give coffee, tea, or alcoholic beverages. When the victim's temperature remains at a safe level, put the victim to bed and get medical help.

For mild heat exhaustion, provide bed rest. Give a salt solution (1/2 teaspoon salt—about 2 "pinches"—in 1/2 glass of water) every 15 minutes for 3 or 4 doses. Medical care is needed for severe heat exhaustion.

It may be hard to remember the names of the two conditions, but it should be easy to remember this: A victim who is very hot and not sweating (heat stroke) must be cooled off quickly, but a victim who is sweating, has a normal temperature, and is tired (heat exhaustion) needs rest but does not need to be cooled off so vigorously.

28. How should you care for a victim of heat stroke?

☒ a. Provide immediate cooling.
[ ] b. Provide mild exercise.


29. What are the signs of heat stroke?

[ ] a. Pale, clammy skin, profuse sweating, normal body temperature.
☒ b. Hot, dry skin, little or no sweating, high body temperature.


30. Lower the body temperature of a heat stroke victim until it is at a safe level—about

☒ a. $39^{\circ}C$ ($102^{\circ}F$).
[ ] b. $41^{\circ}C$ ($106^{\circ}F$).

Answers:

28.  a.  Provide immediate cooling for a victim of heat stroke.


29.  b.  Hot, dry skin, little or no sweating, and high body temperature
         are the signs of heat stroke.


30.  a.  Lower the body temperature to about $39^\circ$C ($102^\circ$F).

31. A young man becomes nauseated after road construction work on a hot day. His skin is hot and dry, and his body temperature is high. What should you do?

[ ] a. Put him to bed and give him salt water to drink.
[x] b. Cool him quickly by immersing him in cool water or sponging him all over with cool water or alcohol.


32. An older woman becomes very tired while mowing her lawn on a hot day. Her skin is cool and wet with perspiration, and she vomits. What should you do?

[x] a. Put her to bed and give her salt water to drink.
[ ] b. Cool her quickly by immersing her in cool water or sponging her all over with cool water or alcohol.

Answers:

31.  b.  Cool the man <u>quickly</u>!

32.  a.  Put her to bed and give her salt water to drink.

## Heat Cramps

Heat cramps usually involve the abdominal muscles or the limbs; heat cramps may accompany heat exhaustion.

Firm pressure, and warm, wet towels placed over the cramped area give relief. Give a salt water solution to drink, as you would for heat exhaustion.

266

## Frostbite

Frostbite results from freezing a part of the body. Usually the frozen area is small. The nose, ears, cheeks, fingers, and toes are affected most often. People with poor circulation, such as the elderly and the exhausted, are not as resistant to cold as young people. Intoxicated persons sometimes suffer extensive injury.

Just before frostbite occurs, the skin may be slightly flushed. As frostbite develops, the skin changes to white or grayish-yellow. Blisters may appear later. Pain sometimes is felt early but subsides later. Often there is no pain; the part feels intensely cold and numb. The victim frequently is not aware of frostbite until pale, glossy skin is observed.

First aid for frostbite is to bring the victim indoors and rewarm the areas quickly in water between $39^\circ$C and $41^\circ$C ($102^\circ$F — $105^\circ$F). Give a warm drink—not coffee, tea, or alcohol. The victim should not smoke. Smoking tends to constrict the blood vessels in the skin, making the injury slow to heal. Keep the frozen parts in warm water or covered with warm cloths for 30 minutes, even though the tissue will be very painful as it thaws. Then elevate the injured area and protect it from injury. Do not allow blisters to be broken. Use sterile, soft, dry material to cover the injured areas. A small amount of dry, sterile cotton or gauze can be placed between injured fingers and toes. Keep the victim warm and get immediate medical care.

If the victim will have to use the frostbitten part to get to safety, or if it will not be possible to keep the victim warm, do not rewarm the part. When you get to a safe place, warm the part quickly.

After thawing, the victim should try to move the injured areas a little, but no more than can be done alone, without help.

— Do <u>not</u> rub the frostbitten part. This may cause gangrene (tissue death).

— Do <u>not</u> use ice, snow, gasoline, or <u>anything</u> cold on frostbite.

— Do <u>not</u> use heat lamps or hot water bottles to rewarm the part.

— Do <u>not</u> place the part near a hot stove.

The first aider should be very friendly and encouraging, since rewarmed frostbite is painful and frightening looking.

33.  Before obtaining medical care for frostbite,

[X]  a.  warm the part quickly.  Do not rub or break blisters.
[ ]  b.  rub the area vigorously to stimulate circulation.


34.  A frostbitten part should be warmed

[ ]  a.  in very hot water or near a fire.
[X]  b.  gently and treated gently.

Answers:

33.  a.  Warm the part quickly.  Do not rub or break blisters.


34.  b.  Frostbite should be warmed <u>gently</u> and treated <u>gently</u>.

## Exposure to Cold

When a person who is poorly protected is exposed to cold for a long time, the body temperature will fall. Death can result. The victim of exposure becomes sleepy and numb, movement is difficult, eyesight fails. The person may stagger or fall; finally he or she becomes unconscious.

Bring the victim indoors into a warm area quickly, or make an emergency shelter where first aid can be given. Provide rapid but gentle rewarming. Remove wet or cold garments and provide warm, dry clothing or covering. Dry the person thoroughly. If the victim reacts and becomes conscious, give a hot drink.

If a warm area is not available, and the victim's body temperature is low, wrapping the victim alone in blankets or a sleeping bag will not help. Wrap the victim, together with warm water bottles, warm stones, or persons who are warm, in blankets or a sleeping bag. Take care not to burn someone who is not fully conscious.

The victim of frostbite or exposure must be kept warm after first aid. Anyone who has suffered ill effects from heat or cold should have medical care.

35.   What is most important for a victim of exposure to cold?

[x]   a.  Immediate warming.
[ ]   b.  Immediate cooling.


36.   What can you do if the victim cannot be treated in a warm area?

[ ]   a.  Wrap the victim in blankets or a sleeping bag.
[x]   b.  Wrap warm objects or other persons inside blankets
          or a sleeping bag with the victim.

Answers:

35.   a.  Immediate warming is important for a victim of exposure to cold.


36.   b.  Wrap warm objects or other persons inside blankets or a
          sleeping bag with the victim.


\*    \*    \*


Now you will have a break.  When you return, continue

with Unit 4 in the workbook.

# UNIT 4

## ESCAPING FROM FIRE

### Planning

Plan with your family at least two ways to get out of every room in your home. Procedures for some commercial buildings are different from those for houses. Find out how escape and reporting are to be handled for commercial buildings that you regularly use.

It is a good idea to place fire extinguishers and smoke and fire detectors in several locations about the home and office. Contact local authorities for information about fire prevention.

## Escape

If you are in a house and smell smoke or see fire, get out quickly. Leave a burning house before turning in a fire alarm. When you reach a telephone in a safe place, call the fire emergency number. Give the fire department the address of the fire and your name. Wait for the fire department to hang up the telephone first.

Before opening a door in a burning building, feel the door quickly with the palm or the back of your hand. If the door is hot, the room on the other side is probably on fire.

If the door is cool, kneel down and check the air coming under the door. If the air is cool, the room may be safe to enter.

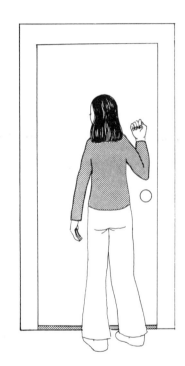

Kneel behind the door while you open it just a little with your face turned away from the opening. Listen and smell for fire and smoke. If the room behind the door is on fire, very hot air and gases may explode when the door is opened. If smoke and hot air rush into the room that you are in, shut the door fast.

Close all doors and windows behind you as you leave. When leaving a smoke-filled area, move quickly but crawl on your hands and knees. Hot air, carbon monoxide, and many other poisonous gases are likely to rise, while other gases may lie near the floor. For those reasons, the air will be fresher about one foot above the floor.

Use a stairway instead of an elevator to escape from a burning building. The fire may damage the elevator and trap you inside.

If you cannot escape quickly, protect your hands, face, and breathing passages with wet cloths and wet clothing. If you are trapped in the building, open a window a little and hang something out of it—a shirt, sheet, towel, or anything else that will show and attract attention. This small opening in the window will give you some fresh air, and something hanging outside will let the people outside know that someone is in the building. Wait to be rescued.

If your clothes catch fire, roll on the floor or ground to put out the flames. If someone else's clothes are burning, make the person lie down and roll. Smother the fire.

1.  Before opening a door of a burning building, you put your hand
    on the door to see if it is hot.  If it is not hot,

[X]  a.  kneel and feel for hot air at the bottom edge of the door.
[ ]  b.  it is safe to open the door and walk into the next room.


2.  If you cannot feel hot air coming under the door,

[X]  a.  kneel behind the door and open it slowly.
[ ]  b.  open the door and walk into the next room.


3.  If your clothes catch fire,

[ ]  a.  run.
[X]  b.  roll on the floor or ground.
[ ]  c.  take off the burning clothing.


4.  In a burning building, the safest air to breathe is usually

[ ]  a.  near the ceiling.
[X]  b.  about one foot above the floor.

Answers:

1.    a.  If the door is not hot, <u>kneel and feel for hot air</u> at the bottom edge of the door.

2.    a.  If you cannot feel hot air coming under the door, <u>kneel behind the door and open it slowly</u>.

3.    b.  If your clothes catch fire, <u>roll on the floor or ground</u>.

4.    b.  The safest air is usually <u>about one foot above the floor</u>.

\*    \*    \*

Continue with the workbook lesson on electrical emergencies.

# ELECTRICAL EMERGENCIES

An electric shock may be caused by damaged or misused wires in the home, by high-tension wires, or by lightning. Electric shock can cause the victim to become unconscious, and it may stop the heart or breathing. Electricity can also cause severe burns.

Do not approach or touch a victim of electric shock until you can do so safely. If an emergency is caused by a tool, an appliance, or by wiring, turn off the electricity at a fuse box if possible. If you cannot shut off the current, you may be able to roll the victim away from the wire or the tool with materials that do not conduct electricity. A long, dry wooden handle can be used to disconnect an electric plug.

As soon as a victim of electric shock is rescued and in a safe place, check to see if mouth-to-mouth breathing or cardiopulmonary resuscitation (CPR) is needed. After breathing and heartbeat are restored, check for other injuries, or have a second or third person check for other injuries. Keep the victim lying down and comfortable, maintain normal body temperature, and give first aid for burns and other injuries. Treat electrical burns the same way you treat heat burns. Keep the victim from moving until medical personnel can take him or her to a hospital.

Do not approach any area where a high voltage wire is down. Send for help from the utility company. If an electric wire falls on an automobile or other vehicle, calm the people inside. Convince people to stay inside, without touching the metal or the outside parts of the vehicle, until professional rescue workers arrive. If there is extreme danger to the vehicle from fire or other hazard, people may try jumping. If they must jump, they should get away from the vehicle and away from the wire, without touching the vehicle and the ground at the same time. Jumping is very dangerous.

5.  What do you do <u>first</u> after rescuing an unconscious victim of electric shock?

[ ]  a.  Call an ambulance and treat for shock.
[X]  b.  Check breathing and heartbeat.


6.  If a person receives an electric shock,

[X]  a.  do <u>not</u> touch the person before stopping the electric current.
[ ]  b.  give mouth-to-mouth breathing, then stop the electricity.


7.  What is the important thing to remember when there is
    a fallen electric wire?

[ ]  a.  Do not jump near other persons.
[X]  b.  Do not go anywhere near the wire.

Answers:

5.    b. <u>Check breathing and heartbeat</u> after you rescue an unconscious
       victim of electric shock.

6.    a. Do <u>not</u> touch the person before you stop the electricity.

7.    b. Do not go anywhere near the fallen wire.

*   *   *

Continue with the workbook lesson on exposure to radiation.

## EXPOSURE TO RADIATION

You can give first aid to a person who has been exposed to radiation with little hazard to yourself, if the person has not been externally contaminated by radioactive particles. You can take special precautions to make it safer to handle persons and objects that are contaminated by radioactive particles.

Radioactive particles can be washed off the hair, the body, and closed food containers. Food left uncovered or lightly covered in the open is not safe. Throw away clothing that has been contaminated by radioactive particles. Radioactive particles may remain in clothing and other fabric, even after they are washed. When you give first aid to a person who has been contaminated by radioactive particles, wear disposable clothing, and wrap the victim in a blanket that is not contaminated.

Give first aid for injuries, then call a medical center—preferably a center that is authorized for care of radiation accidents—to let them know that you are bringing in a radiation victim. The victim of a radiation accident should be taken to radiation medical facilities whether injured or not. If you have given first aid in a radiation emergency, the medical center may want to check you also.

Radioactive particles become less dangerous with the passage of time. Some become less dangerous very rapidly; others take many years.

8.  If you give first aid to a person who has been exposed to radiation, but not
    contaminated by radioactive particles, there will normally be

[ ]  a. a great hazard to you.
[X]  b. little hazard to you.


9.  You can safely remove radioactive particles by washing them from
    (check more than one)

[X]  a. your hair.
[ ]  b. food left uncovered in the open.
[X]  c. your body.
[X]  d. closed containers of food.
[ ]  e. clothing.


10.  Take a radiation victim to a radiation medical facility

[ ]  a. only if care is needed for injuries.
[X]  b. whether or not care is needed for injuries.

290

Answers:

8.  b.  There will normally be <u>little hazard to you</u> if you give first aid
        to a radiation victim.

9.      You can wash radioactive particles off

[X]  a.  your hair.
[ ]  b.  food left uncovered in the open.
[X]  c.  your body.
[X]  d.  closed containers of food.
[ ]  e.  clothing.

10. b.  Take the victim to a radiation medical facility
        <u>whether or not</u> care is needed for injuries.

*     *     *

Continue with the workbook lesson on obtaining help in an emergency.

# OBTAINING HELP IN AN EMERGENCY

## Medical Help

The victim of a serious accident or illness should always have medical care even if he or she seems to feel fine.  Call for medical help, send for help, or take the victim to a medical facility as soon as it is reasonable to do so.

If an emergency occurs near a telephone, you may be able to call right away. In a remote location you may examine the victim and give extensive first aid before being able to send for help.

You may be the only person giving first aid.  If you have to stay to keep a victim alive and cannot telephone for help, then stay and hope someone comes along to help. If, after thorough checking, the victim does not appear to need constant attention, you might decide to go for help or take the victim to medical help.

If you are the first aider in charge, stay in charge until you can turn the victim over to authorities, such as a doctor, rescue squad, or police, or to relatives of the victim. Tell them what happened, what the victim said, what the witnesses saw, and what has been done for the victim. Give this information only to someone in authority who needs to know. Give only necessary information and directions to bystanders. Do not discuss the victim's condition with the victim or with witnesses.

In many emergencies, other people will be around to help. An untrained person can follow your directions to do many things, such as preparing bandages, applying direct pressure to a wound, tying a bandage, and helping carry a victim to safety. An untrained person may be able to give mouth-to-mouth breathing after learning from watching you. Some of the most important things an untrained person can do are to get help, direct traffic, and keep people who are not helping away from victims.

## Medical Identification

Some people who have conditions such as diabetes, epilepsy, and heart disease have medical identification. Give urgent care, then look for a card, bracelet, or neck chain that tells you what might be wrong and what to do. The instructions may tell you to give the victim medicine or give you a phone number to call. Tell anyone else who is there what you have found.

If you look in a victim's wallet or purse, try to have a witness. This can protect both you and the victim from embarrassment.

295

11. When should you look for medical identification?

[ ] a. Before you give urgent care.
[X] b. After you give urgent care.
[ ] c. After the victim wakes up.


12. Which would be better to say to a burn victim?

[ ] a. "You have a third degree burn on your leg. I'll bandage it."
[X] b. "I'll bandage your burn and make you more comfortable."


13. You rescue a man from the water and find that he is not breathing. When you tip his head back, he starts to breathe again. He wakes up after a few minutes and says he feels better. Should he see a doctor?

[X] a. Yes.
[ ] b. Not if he feels fine now.

296

Answers:

11.   b.  Look for medical identification <u>after you give urgent care</u>.

12.   b.  "I'll bandage your burn and make you more comfortable."
         Talking about a third degree burn will not help keep the victim calm.

13.   a.  <u>Yes</u>, anyone whose breathing has stopped, even for a very short time,
         should see a doctor.

## Emergency Services

Many cities use 911 as an emergency telephone number. It is the fastest way to get the police, the fire department, the rescue squad, or an ambulance.

If your community does not have an emergency number, write down all important numbers near your telephone. These numbers will include the fire department, police, hospital, poison control center, and ambulance or rescue squad. If you get caught without an emergency number, call the telephone operator. When you travel, find out emergency numbers where you are staying.

When you phone for help, be sure you are talking to the right person.  Then tell

     — what happened.

     — what is being done.

     — what you need.

     — your name, location, and the phone number you are calling from.

     — the number of persons involved.

<u>Don't hang up first</u>.  The person you are talking to may need more information.

Let the person on the other end hang up first.

14. A first aider phoned for emergency help and said, "My name is George Jones, and my home number is 123-4567. Two people have been hit by a car outside my house. They have some broken bones. They are breathing; I have stopped serious bleeding. I need an ambulance." Then George hung up.

George did two things wrong on the phone. What were they?

He _hung_ _up_ _first_ and he

didn't tell _his address_ .

15. What information do you give when you phone for help?

What _happened_ .

What is _being_ _done_ .

What _you_ _need_ .

Your name, location, and _phone #_ _____ .

The _#_ _7_ _persons_ involved.

Answers:

14. George <u>hung up first</u> and he didn't tell his <u>location</u> (<u>where he was</u>).

15. Tell what <u>happened</u>.
    Tell what is <u>being done</u>.
    Tell what <u>you need</u>.
    Tell your name, location, and <u>phone number</u>.
    Tell the <u>number of persons</u> involved.

\*    \*    \*

Now you will see the films on emergency rescue.

## RESCUE AND TRANSFER

Rescue

One of your first decisions in an emergency is whether or not to move the victim.

You must consider these factors:

— Danger of injury you can cause by moving the victim.

— Danger to you and the victim from the surroundings, such as from fire, water, and passing automobiles.

— Danger to the victim from existing injuries and other conditions, such as severe bleeding or stopped breathing.

302

Don't move a victim if you don't have to. If there is danger, get the victim and yourself to a safe place before you do anything else. If the victim must be dragged, pull the long way by the shoulders or, if necessary, by the feet. Do not pull sideways. Once you are both out of danger, keep the victim still. Do not let an injured person get up and walk around.

First make any <u>necessary</u> rescue. Then, if the person is not conscious, check for breathing and heartbeat and stop severe bleeding before you care for other conditions.

16. You find an unconscious woman in a burning car. Her leg is bleeding heavily. What do you do first?

[X] a. Get her out of and away from the car.
[ ] b. Stop the bleeding and check her breathing.


17. A man who is trapped in a car is not breathing. There is no sign of fire and the car is off the highway. What do you do first?

[ ] a. Get him out of and away from the car.
[X] b. Give mouth-to-mouth breathing.


18. What do you check for almost as soon as you check for breathing and heartbeat?

[ ] a. Broken bones.
[ ] b. Shock.
[X] c. Bleeding.

Answers:

16.   a.  Get her out of and away from the car first.

17.   b.  Give mouth-to-mouth breathing first.

18.   c.  Check for <u>bleeding</u> almost as soon as you check for breathing and heartbeat.

19. An accident victim is conscious, has a broken arm, and blood is gushing from a big cut on the leg. What do you do <u>first</u>?

[ ]  a.  Splint the arm.
[X]  b.  Stop the bleeding.
[ ]  c.  Check for breathing.

20. A man falls and hits his head on the corner of a table. His forehead is bleeding heavily. He is unconscious. What will you do <u>first</u>?

[ ]  a.  Stop the bleeding and raise his head and shoulders.
[X]  b.  Check for breathing and heartbeat. Apply direct
       pressure to the wound as quickly as you can.

Answers:

19.  b.  <u>Stop the bleeding</u> first.  You do not need to check for breathing because the victim is conscious.

20.  b.  Check for <u>breathing and heartbeat</u> first.  Apply direct pressure as soon as possible.

## Moving a Victim

Perhaps more harm is done through improper transportation than through any other measure associated with emergency aid.  Any time you must move a victim, be careful to keep injured body parts from twisting, bending, and shaking.

If you must lift someone to safety before checking for injuries, protect all parts of the body from the forces of lifting.  Support the arms and legs, the head, and the back.  Keep the body in a straight line.

People who may have head injuries, back injuries, or fractures of the leg or pelvis should be moved lying down, with the injured parts immobilized (splinted) and the body tied to a backboard.

Sometimes an injured part cannot be immobilized until the victim has been moved a short distance. If a limb is injured, hold the broken part to keep it from moving or twisting: Place one hand just above the injured area and one just below it. Keep the injury from bending and twisting, while helpers lift the body and another helper keeps the adjacent joints from moving.

It is difficult for inexperienced people to lift and carry a person gently. They may not work together smoothly. Give them careful directions. It is wise to practice moving an uninjured person first, before moving the victim.

Any transfer will be harmful unless the injured parts are immobilized. Put splints and backboards on victims before they are moved at all unless there is <u>urgent</u> danger. It is usually best to wait until a trained rescue crew is available.

21.  A young woman has a broken leg.  If danger requires that she be moved before splinting, what precautions should be taken while moving her?

[X]  a.  Hold the broken bones and the adjacent joints as still as possible.
[ ]  b.  Help her to walk by holding the shoulders of the two persons she is walking between.

22.  You discover a man lying near a burning automobile and gasping for breath. You do <u>not</u> lift him by the belt because

[ ]  a.  the belt may not be strong enough to support the man's weight.
[X]  b.  he may have chest or back injuries; lifting him by the belt could cause further injury.

23.  You have other people to help you transport an injured person.  You show them how, tell them how, and

[ ]  a.  practice by moving the victim.
[X]  b.  practice by moving an uninjured person.

Answers:

21.   a.  Hold the broken bones and the adjacent joints as still as possible.

22.   b.  The man may have chest or back injuries; lifting him by the belt could cause further injury.

23.   b.  Practice on another person before you move the victim.

*   *   *

Take the final test when your instructor tells you to begin.

# FINAL TEST

## Form A

Take this test in class when your instructor tells you
to begin.  Mark only one answer to each question.
Please do not look back at the workbook while you
take the test.

Your instructor may give you Test Form B instead of
Form A.  Form B covers the same basic material.

1. Can you tell how serious a gunshot wound is by looking at the surface of the wound?

[ ] a. Yes.
[X] b. No.


2. If you suspect a fracture of the lower leg, what parts do you keep from moving?

[ ] a. Hip, ankle, broken bone ends.
[ ] b. Broken bone ends, ankle, knee.
[X] c. Hip, ankle, knee.


3. If something seems to be embedded or stuck into an eye,

[X] a. bandage both eyes and get medical help.
[ ] b. lift the object out with the corner of a clean cloth.

4. How do you check for breathing?

[ ] a. Look at the pupils of the eyes.
[ ] b. Check to see if the person's heart is beating.
[X] c. Listen for breathing and feel for air at the mouth.
     See if the chest is moving.


5. To give abdominal thrusts to an unconscious person, place the heel of one hand

[ ] a. below the waist.
[ ] b. over the rib cage.
[X] c. between the rib cage and the waist.


6. Give abdominal thrusts

[ ] a. downward, toward the ground.
[X] b. inward and upward, toward the lungs.

7. Describe the first steps for mouth-to-mouth breathing:

A = Airway: _Tilt Lead_ and _check for breathing_.

Quick = _4 full breaths_.

Check = _breathing_ and _pluse_.

8. A woman who has just been in an auto accident feels pain and tenderness in her back. You do not see any signs of injury. What do you do?

[X] a. Keep her from moving.
[ ] b. Have her walk around to see if that makes her feel better.

9. A woman is bleeding heavily from a cut on the leg. She is unconscious. What do you do first?

[ ] a. Apply direct pressure and elevate the injured leg.
[X] b. Check for breathing and heartbeat. Stop the bleeding as soon as you can.

10. What do you do first after rescuing a victim of electric shock?

[ ]  a. Call an ambulance.
[ ]  b. Give care to prevent shock.
[X]  c. Check breathing and heartbeat.

11. How do you help an <u>unconscious</u> victim of poisoning who is breathing?

[X]  a. Call the poison center.
[ ]  b. Give water or milk to drink.
[ ]  c. Cause vomiting.

12. If a person receives an electric shock,

[ ]  a. give mouth-to-mouth breathing right away. Then stop the electric current.
[X]  b. do <u>not</u> touch the person before you stop the electric current.

13. An older woman seems to be unable to move one side of her body. Her speech is hard to understand. You think she may have had

[X] a. a stroke.
[ ] b. a heart attack.
[ ] c. heat exhaustion.

14. What kinds of wounds should a first aider wash?

[ ] a. Only large, dirty wounds.
[X] b. Only small wounds.
[ ] c. All wounds.

15. A blunt injury of the eye

[ ] a. needs medical care only if the eye is very bruised and swollen.
[X] b. must have immediate medical care.

16. The first time you checked an injured man, he was conscious.
    Do you need to check again later for consciousness?

[X]  a. Yes.
[ ]  b. No.


17. If you cannot inflate the victim's lungs the first time you try
    to give 4 quick breaths,

[ ]  a. give 4 thrusts.
[X]  b. retip the head and try again.


18. What method of controlling bleeding should you use only if nothing
    else works?

[ ]  a. Direct pressure.
[X]  b. Tourniquet.
[ ]  c. Pressure point.

318

19. Will an arm pressure point control bleeding from the head?

[ ] a. Yes.
[x] b. No.


20. Bleeding from most wounds is controlled best and most easily by

[ ] a. pressure points.
[ ] b. a tourniquet.
[x] c. direct pressure.


21. Is there anything you can do to reduce the chance of heart attack or stroke?

[ ] a. No, the tendency to those conditions is inherited.
[x] b. Yes, keep in good physical condition and don't smoke.

22. If a victim of choking is <u>still conscious</u>, and 4 back blows and 4 thrusts fail on the first try, you should

[ ] a. try to give four quick breaths.
[X] b. keep giving back blows and thrusts.
[ ] c. go for help.


23. When you use the head tip—neck lift, you apply the major force with your hand that is

[ ] a. under the neck
[X] b. on the forehead.

24. Which position is best for someone who is awake but may be in shock?

[ ] a. Lying face down.
[ ] b. Sitting up with the head forward.
[X] c. On the back with the feet raised.

25. If you cannot tell for sure how deep a burn is, you should assume that it is a

[X] a. deep burn.
[ ] b. thin burn.


26. What is the first aid treatment for a sprain?

[X] a. The same as for a fracture.
[ ] b. Rest. Frequent, mild exercise.


27. Is a small, second-degree burn on a critical area serious?

[X] a. Yes.
[ ] b. No.

28. If you think there may be an object in an unconscious man's airway, what is the correct order of first aid steps?

[ ] a. Sweep in the mouth, give 4 back blows, try to give breaths, give 4 thrusts.
[X] b. Try to give breaths, give 4 back blows, give 4 thrusts, sweep in the mouth.

29. Remove all clothing from the area of a burn that was caused by

[X] a. a chemical.
[ ] b. fire.

30. What is the first step for a <u>conscious</u> victim of poisoning?

[X] a. Call the poison center.
[ ] b. Give water or milk to drink.
[ ] c. Cause vomiting.

31.  If there is immediate danger from the surroundings, what precautions
     should be taken before moving a person with a broken leg?

[X]  a.  Hold the broken bones and adjacent joints as still as possible,
         then move the person.
[ ]  b.  Help the person to walk with the support of two other persons
         at the shoulders.


32.  Wash a chemical off the skin for at least

[ ]  a.  1 minute.
[X]  b.  5 minutes.
[ ]  c.  15 minutes.


33.  Wash a chemical out of an eye for at least

[ ]  a.  1 minute.
[ ]  b.  5 minutes.
[X]  c.  15 minutes.

34. A member of a highway work crew becomes nauseated while working in the sun on a hot day. The person has hot, dry skin and a high body temperature. What care is necessary <u>immediately</u>?

[ ]  a. Have the person sit down for a while and have a cool drink.
[X] b. Cool quickly by putting water all over the person and the person's clothing.

35. You are bandaging an open burn that has fire-charred clothing in it. You should

[X] a. bandage over the clothing.
[ ]  b. remove the clothing before you bandage it.

36. When you do the head tip—chin lift, lift the chin

[ ]  a. firmly, at the soft part of the throat.
[X] b. gently, at the bony point of the jaw.

37. A baseball player has a bruise on his head and was unconscious for
a few seconds. He is awake now. You should

[ ] a. assume that he is probably all right now, because he is awake.
[x] b. suspect that he may have a serious head injury and get medical advice.

38. You cannot tell whether a victim's ankle is broken or sprained.
Do you give first aid for a broken ankle?

[x] a. Yes.
[ ] b. No.

39. What do you do first for a chemical burn of the skin?

[x] a. Wash the chemical off.
[ ] b. Try to find out how to neutralize the chemical.

40.   Which burns may be cooled directly in water?

[X]   a.  Small, thin burns with no open tissue.
[ ]   b.  Large, deep burns with open tissue.


41.   If you are giving breaths to a baby, how big is a puff?

[ ]   a.  A breath of moderate size.
[X]   b.  The amount of air you can hold in your cheeks.


42.   After giving A Quick Check, give one puff to a baby every

[X]   a.  3 seconds.
[ ]   b.  5 seconds.

43.   What is the most important thing to do for any victim of convulsions?

[ ]   a. Give fluids to drink.
[X]   b. Give mouth-to-mouth or mouth-to-nose breathing if necessary.
[ ]   c. Recommend mild exercise.


44.   What are the four critical areas of the body for burns?

[ ]   a. Hands, feet, arms, and legs.
[X]   b. Hands, feet, face, and genitals.
[ ]   c. Feet, legs, genitals, and torso.
[ ]   d. Feet, face, arms, and legs.


45.   An important part of care for frostbite is to

[ ]   a. rub it vigorously to stimulate circulation.
[X]   b. provide immediate gentle warming.
[ ]   c. put ice on the frozen parts.
[ ]   d. break the blisters.

46. An unconscious victim of head injuries should be checked frequently to see if

[ ] a. bandages need to be changed.
[X] b. mouth-to-mouth breathing is needed.


47. After you have given 4 quick breaths, how often do you give breaths to an adult?

[ ] a. Once every 3 seconds.
[X] b. Once every 5 seconds.


48. A victim of a radiation accident should be taken to a radiation medical facility

[X] a. always.
[ ] b. only if care is needed for injuries.

49. A person who has been in the sun feels ill, is <u>sweating</u>, and has a <u>normal</u> body temperature. What is the first aid?

[X] a. Rest in the shade. Give salt water to drink.
[ ] b. Pour cool water all over the body.


50. Which cut has a higher risk of infection?

[ ] a. A shallow cut that bleeds freely.
[X] b. A small, deep cut that bleeds very little.